MW00634705

STAAR
Grade 6 Math Practice

GET DIGITAL ACCESS TO

 2 STAAR Tests

 Personalized Study Plans

REGISTER NOW

Link	QR Code

Visit the link below for online registration

lumoslearning.com/a/tedbooks

Access Code: G6MSTAAR-40751-P

State of Texas Assessments of Academic Readiness (STAAR) Test Practice: 6th Grade Math Practice Workbook and Full-length Online Assessments: Texas Test Study Guide

Contributing Editor - Renee Bade
Contributing Editor - Kimberly G.
Executive Producer - Mukunda Krishnaswamy
Program Director - Anirudh Agarwal
Designer and Illustrator - Snehal Sharan

COPYRIGHT ©2021 by Lumos Information Services, LLC. ALL RIGHTS RESERVED. No portion of this book may be reproduced mechanically, electronically or by any other means, including photocopying, recording, taping, Web Distribution or Information Storage and Retrieval systems, without prior written permission of the Publisher, Lumos Information Services, LLC.

State of Texas Assessment of Academic Readinesss is not affiliated to Lumos Learning. The Texas Department of Education , was not involved in the production of, and does not endorse these products or this site.

ISBN 10: 1949855325

ISBN 13: 978-1949855326

Printed in the United States of America

FOR SCHOOL EDITION AND PERMISSIONS, CONTACT US

LUMOS INFORMATION SERVICES, LLC

 PO Box 1575, Piscataway, NJ 08855-1575
 www.LumosLearning.com

Email: support@lumoslearning.com
Tel: (732) 384-0146
Fax: (866) 283-6471

Lumos Learning
Step Up Your Skills

INTRODUCTION

This book is specifically designed to improve student achievement on the State of Texas Assessment of Academic Readiness (STAAR). Students perform at their best on standardized tests when they feel comfortable with the test content as well as the test format. Lumos online practice tests are meticulously designed to mirror the state assessment. They adhere to the guidelines provided by the state for the number of sessions and questions, standards, difficulty level, question types, test duration and more.

Based on our decade of experience developing practice resources for standardized tests, we've created a dynamic system, the Lumos Smart Test Prep Methodology. It provides students with realistic assessment rehearsal and an efficient pathway to overcoming each proficiency gap.

Use the Lumos Smart Test Prep Methodology to achieve a high score on the STAAR.

Lumos Smart Test Prep Methodology

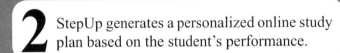

START
Practice Test-1
Practice Test-2
FINISH

Targeted Practice → Actual STAAR → Personalized Study Plan

1 The student takes the first online diagnostic test, which assesses proficiency levels in various standards.

2 StepUp generates a personalized online study plan based on the student's performance.

3 The student completes targeted practice in the printed workbook and marks it as complete in the online study plan.

4 The student then attempts the second online practice test.

5 StepUp generates a second individualized online study plan.

6 The student completes the targeted practice and is ready for the actual STAAR

Table of Contents

Chapter 1

Numerical Representations and Relationships

Chapter 1

Lesson 1: Classification of Numbers

1. **Which of the following are integers?**

   Ⓐ -3
   Ⓑ $\frac{1}{4}$
   Ⓒ 7
   Ⓓ 0.454545...

2. **Which of the following statements is true?**

   Ⓐ Every rational number is an integer.
   Ⓑ Every whole number is a rational number.
   Ⓒ Every irrational number is a natural number.
   Ⓓ Every rational number is a whole number.

3. **Which of the following accurately describes the square root of 10?**

   Ⓐ It is rational.
   Ⓑ It is irrational.
   Ⓒ It is an integer.
   Ⓓ It is a whole number.

4. **Complete the following statement: Pi is _____.**

   Ⓐ both real and rational
   Ⓑ real but not rational
   Ⓒ rational but not real
   Ⓓ neither real nor rational

5. **Complete the following statement: $\sqrt{7}$ is _____.**

   Ⓐ both a real and a rational number
   Ⓑ a real number, but not rational
   Ⓒ a rational number, but not a real number
   Ⓓ neither a real nor a rational number

6. The number 57 belongs to which of the following set(s) of numbers?

   Ⓐ N only
   Ⓑ N, W, and Z only
   Ⓒ N, W, Z, and Q only
   Ⓓ All of the following: N, W, Z, Q, and R

7. From the following set: $\{-\sqrt{5.7}, -9, 0, 5.25, 3i, \sqrt{16}\}$
   Select the answer choice that shows the elements which are Natural numbers.

   Ⓐ $-\sqrt{5.7}$, -9, 0, 5.25, 3i, $\sqrt{16}$
   Ⓑ $-\sqrt{5.7}$, -9, 0, 5.25, 3i
   Ⓒ 3i
   Ⓓ Positive square root of 16

8. From the following set: $\{-\sqrt{5.7}, -9, 0, 5.25, 3i, \sqrt{16}\}$
   Select the answer choice that shows the elements that are Rational numbers.

   Ⓐ $-\sqrt{5.7}$, -9, 0, 5.25, 3i, $\sqrt{16}$
   Ⓑ -9, 0, 5.25, $\sqrt{16}$
   Ⓒ 3i
   Ⓓ $-\sqrt{5.7}$

9. Which of the numbers below are irrational?

   Ⓐ $\sqrt{169}$
   Ⓑ $\sqrt{8}$
   Ⓒ $\sqrt{16}$
   Ⓓ $\sqrt{3}$

10. Write the repeating rational number 0.1515... as a fraction.

Lesson 2: Opposites & Absolute Values

1. Larissa has $4\frac{1}{2}$ cups of flour. She is making cookies using a recipe that calls for $2\frac{3}{4}$ cups of flour. After baking the cookies how much flour will be left?

   Ⓐ $2\frac{3}{4}$ cups

   Ⓑ $2\frac{1}{4}$ cups

   Ⓒ $2\frac{3}{8}$ cups

   Ⓓ $1\frac{3}{4}$ cups

2. The accounting ledger for the high school band showed a balance of $2,123. They purchased new uniforms for a total of $2,400. How much must they deposit into their account in order to prevent it from being overdrawn?

   Ⓐ $382
   Ⓑ $462
   Ⓒ $4,000
   Ⓓ $277

3. Juan is climbing a ladder. He begins on the first rung, climbs up four rungs, but then slides down two rungs. What rung is Juan on?

4. **Which of these numbers would be found closest to 0 on a number line?**

   Ⓐ   −5

   Ⓑ $-5\frac{1}{2}$

   Ⓒ $4\frac{1}{2}$

   Ⓓ   −4

5. **On a number line, how far apart are the numbers −5.5 and 7.5?**

   Ⓐ   13 units
   Ⓑ   12 units
   Ⓒ   12.5 units
   Ⓓ   2 units

6. **Which numbers does the following number line represent?**

   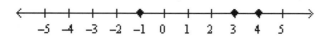

   Ⓐ   {−2, 0, 5}
   Ⓑ   {−3, −1, 4}
   Ⓒ   {−1, 3, 5}
   Ⓓ   {−1, 3, 4}

7. **Evaluate the following: $17 - |(7)(-3)|$**

   Ⓐ   38
   Ⓑ   −4
   Ⓒ   4
   Ⓓ   13

8. **Evaluate the following: $16 + |(7)(-3) - 44| - 5$**

   Ⓐ   76
   Ⓑ   86
   Ⓒ   34
   Ⓓ   44

9. Evaluate the following: $|15 - 47| + 9 - |(-2)(-4) - 17|$

10. Evaluate the following: $18 + 3 |6 - 25| - 11$

Chapter 1

Lesson 3: Using Number Lines

1. **What number does the dot represent on the number line?**

9   16

2. **What number does the dot represent on the number line?**

-5   3

3. **What number does the dot represent on the number line?**

-2   14

4. **What number does the dot represent on the number line?**

-10   -6

  Ⓐ   −5
  Ⓑ   −7.5
  Ⓒ   −8
  Ⓓ   −8.5

5. What number does the dot represent on the number line?

Ⓐ −5
Ⓑ 0
Ⓒ 5
Ⓓ 10

6. Which account balance represents the greatest debt?
   $20, −$45, −$5, $10

   Ⓐ $20
   Ⓑ −$45
   Ⓒ −$5
   Ⓓ $10

7. Which of the following is the warmest temperature?
   5°F above zero, 6°F below zero, 10°F below zero, 2°F above zero

   Ⓐ 5°F above zero
   Ⓑ 6°F below zero
   Ⓒ 10°F below zero
   Ⓓ 2°F above zero

8. Anneliese spent $58.00 on music items and paid $35.00 on a lay-away item. If she has −142.00 left in her account, how much did she start with?

    Ⓐ $−49.00
    Ⓑ $93.00
    Ⓒ $135.00
    Ⓓ −$235.00

9. The Murphys began their summer trip from home at an elevation of 439 feet. They drove to the mountains and climbed to an elevation of 1839 feet. After their visit on the top of the mountain, they drove down the mountainside 527 feet where they stopped for lunch. At the end of the day they spent the night at a campground at an elevation 264 feet higher than the restaurant. What is the difference in elevation between the campground and home?

    Ⓐ 1048 feet
    Ⓑ 1137 feet
    Ⓒ 1576 feet
    Ⓓ 2012 feet

10. Before Tonya went shopping she had $165.00 in her account. She returned a jacket that cost $46.50, bought 2 pairs of socks for $5.99 each, and went to lunch and a movie for $28.00. What is Tonya's account balance now?

    Ⓐ $125.02
    Ⓑ $158.48
    Ⓒ $171.52
    Ⓓ $177.51

Chapter 1

Lesson 4: Rational Numbers in Context

1. Xavier has a golf score of −7 (we write −7 because it is 7 points below par) and Curtis has a golf score of −12. Who has the higher score? Explain your answer.

2. Kelly has read $\frac{5}{6}$ of a book. Helen has read $\frac{9}{12}$ of the same book. Who has read more of the book?

    Ⓐ $\frac{5}{6}$ is more than $\frac{9}{12}$ so Kelly has read more.

    Ⓑ $\frac{5}{6}$ is less than $\frac{9}{12}$ so Helen has read more.

    Ⓒ $\frac{5}{6}$ is the same as $\frac{9}{12}$ so both Kelly and Helen have read the same amount.

    Ⓓ We cannot tell who has read more because the fractions have different denominators.

3. The record low temperature for NY is −52°F. The record low temperature for Alaska is −80°F. Which of the following inequalities accurately compares these two temperatures?

    Ⓐ −52° F < −80° F
    Ⓑ −80° F > −52° F
    Ⓒ −52° F= −80° F
    Ⓓ −52° F > −80° F

4. A cake recipe calls for $1\frac{3}{4}$ cups of soy flour, $\frac{20}{8}$ cups of rice flour and 1.6 cups of wheat flour. Which of the following inequalities compares these three quantities accurately?

   Ⓐ $1.6 < \frac{20}{8} < 1\frac{3}{4}$

   Ⓑ $\frac{20}{8} > 1\frac{3}{4} > 1.6$

   Ⓒ $\frac{20}{8} > 1\frac{3}{4} < 1.6$

   Ⓓ $1\frac{3}{4} > 1.6 > \frac{20}{8}$

5. Doug and Sissy went scuba diving. Doug descended to −143 feet and Sissy descended to −134 feet. Who dove deeper?

   Ⓐ −134 > −143, so Sissy dove deeper.
   Ⓑ −134 < −143, so Doug dove deeper.
   Ⓒ −134 = −143, so neither one dove deeper as they descended the same amount.
   Ⓓ |−143| > |−134|, so Doug dove deeper.

6. At the annual town festival $\frac{4}{15}$ of the vendors sold outdoor items, 0.4 sold clothing or indoor items and $\frac{1}{3}$ sold food. Which of the following inequalities compares these three quantities accurately?

   Ⓐ $0.4 < \frac{4}{15} < \frac{1}{3}$

   Ⓑ $\frac{4}{15} > 0.4 > \frac{1}{3}$

   Ⓒ $0.4 > \frac{1}{3} > \frac{4}{15}$

   Ⓓ $\frac{1}{3} < \frac{4}{15} < 0.4$

7. A school of fish (S1) is spotted in the ocean at 15 feet below sea level. A second school (S2) of fish is spotted at $\frac{33}{3}$ feet below sea level. A third school (S3) of fish is spotted 11.5 feet below sea level. Order these numbers from deepest to shallowest. Note: The symbol > means deeper and < means shallower

   Ⓐ S1 < S3 < S2
   Ⓑ S3 < S2 < S1
   Ⓒ S1 > S3 > S2
   Ⓓ S3 < S1 < S2

8. During the first snowfall of the year, Henderson recorded the snow fall each day. The first day $\frac{4}{5}$ of a foot fell. On the second day $\frac{5}{7}$ of a foot fell. On which day did more snow fall?

   Ⓐ $\frac{4}{5} > \frac{5}{7}$, so more snow fell on the first day.

   Ⓑ $\frac{4}{5} < \frac{5}{7}$, so more snow fell on the second day.

   Ⓒ $\frac{4}{5} = \frac{5}{7}$, so the same amount of snow fell on both days.

   Ⓓ We cannot tell from this information because the fractions have different denominators.

9. Molly has $365 in her savings account. She withdraws $415. Bill has a savings account balance of −$45. Which of the following statements is correct?

   Ⓐ Both Molly and Bill owe the bank some amount.
   Ⓑ Molly owes the bank more than Bill.
   Ⓒ Bill owes the bank more than Molly.
   Ⓓ Neither Molly or Bill owe the bank any money.

10. Jeremiah and Farley each bought 5 boxes of energy bars. Within a week Jeremiah eats $2\frac{5}{6}$ boxes and Farley eats $1\frac{15}{9}$ boxes. Who has more left?

    Ⓐ Jeremiah has more left.
    Ⓑ Farley has more left.
    Ⓒ They both have the same amount left.
    Ⓓ We cannot tell from this information because the mixed numbers have different denominators.

Chapter 1

Lesson 5: Interpreting Fractions

1. Suppose three friends wanted to share four cookies equally. How many cookies would each friend receive?

   Ⓐ $1\frac{1}{3}$

   Ⓑ $\frac{3}{4}$

   Ⓒ $1\frac{3}{4}$

   Ⓓ $\frac{1}{3}$

2. If 18 is divided by 5, which fraction represents the remainder divided by divisor?

   Ⓐ $\frac{3}{18}$

   Ⓑ $\frac{3}{5}$

   Ⓒ $\frac{5}{18}$

   Ⓓ $\frac{1}{3}$

3. If there are 90 minutes in a soccer game and 4 squads of players will share this time equally, how many minutes will each squad play?

   Ⓐ $\frac{22}{4}$

   Ⓑ $22\frac{1}{2}$

   Ⓒ $22\frac{2}{10}$

   Ⓓ $18\frac{4}{22}$

4. Damien has $695 in the bank. He wants to withdraw $\frac{2}{5}$th of his money. If he uses a calculator to figure out this amount, which buttons should he press?

Ⓐ [6] [9] [5] [x] [2] [x] [5] [=]
Ⓑ [6] [9] [5] [÷] [2] [x] [5] [=]
Ⓒ [6] [9] [5] [÷] [2] [÷] [5] [=]
Ⓓ [6] [9] [5] [x] [2] [÷] [5] [=]

5. Five friends are taking a trip in a car. They want to share the driving equally. If the trip takes 7 hours, how long should each friend drive?

Ⓐ $\frac{5}{7}$ of an hour

Ⓑ 1 hour 7 minutes

Ⓒ $1\frac{2}{5}$ hours

Ⓓ 1 hour 2 minutes

6. Which fraction is equivalent to 3 ÷ 10?

Ⓐ $\frac{1}{3}$

Ⓑ $\frac{10}{3}$

Ⓒ $\frac{13}{3}$

Ⓓ $\frac{3}{10}$

7. Which number completes this equation?
$\frac{5}{8} = 5 \div \underline{\quad}$

Ⓐ 13

Ⓑ $\frac{1}{5}$

Ⓒ 8

Ⓓ $\frac{1}{8}$

8. If 9 people want to share a birthday cake equally, what fraction of the cake will each person get? Write your answer as a/b.

9. Which number completes this equation?
   $\frac{4}{7} \times 7 = $ ___

10. Which number completes this equation?
    $\frac{2}{3} = $ ___ $\div 3$

Chapter 1

Lesson 6: Expressing Ratios

1. A school has an enrollment of 600 students. 330 of the students are girls. Express the fraction of students who are boys in simplest terms.

    Ⓐ $\dfrac{12}{20}$

    Ⓑ $\dfrac{11}{20}$

    © $\dfrac{9}{20}$

    Ⓓ $\dfrac{13}{20}$

2. In the 14th century, the Sultan of Brunei noticed that his ratio of emeralds to rubies was the same as the ratio of diamonds to pearls. If he had 85 emeralds, 119 rubies, and 45 diamonds, how many pearls did he have?

    Ⓐ 17
    Ⓑ 22
    © 58
    Ⓓ 63

3. Mr. Fullingham has 75 geese and 125 turkeys. What is the ratio of the number of geese to the total number of birds in simplest terms?

    Ⓐ 75:200
    Ⓑ 3:8
    © 125:200
    Ⓓ 5:8

4. The little league team called the Hawks has 7 brunettes, 5 blonds, and 2 redheads. What is the ratio of redheads to the entire team in simplest terms?

   Ⓐ 2:7
   Ⓑ 2:5
   Ⓒ 2:12
   Ⓓ 1:7

5. The little league team called the Hawks has 7 brunettes, 5 blonds, and 2 redheads. The entire little league division that the Hawks belong to has the same ratio of redheads to everyone else. What is the total number of redheads in that division if the total number of players is 126?

   Ⓐ 9
   Ⓑ 14
   Ⓒ 18
   Ⓓ 24

6. Barnaby decided to count the number of ducks and geese flying south for the winter. The first day he counted 175 ducks and 63 geese. What is the ratio of ducks to the total number of birds flying overhead in simplest terms?

   Ⓐ 175:63
   Ⓑ 175:238
   Ⓒ 25:9
   Ⓓ 25:34

7. Barnaby decided to count the number of ducks and geese flying south for the winter. The first day he counted 175 ducks and 63 geese. By the end of migration, Barnaby had counted 4,725 geese. If the ratio of ducks to geese remained the same (175 to 63), how many ducks did he count?

   Ⓐ 13,125
   Ⓑ 17,850
   Ⓒ 10,695
   Ⓓ 14,750

8. Barbara was baking a cake and could not find her tablespoon measure. The recipe calls for $3\frac{1}{3}$ tablespoons. Each table spoon measure 3 teaspoon. How many teaspoons must Barbara use in order to have the recipe turn out all right?

9. The ratio of girls to boys in a grade is 6 to 5. If there are 24 girls in the grade then how many students are there altogether?

10. The ratio of pencils to pens in a box is 3 to 2. If there are 30 pencils and pens altogether, how many pencils are there?

Chapter 1

Lesson 7: Unit Rates

1. Which is a better price: 5 for $1.00, 4 for 85¢, 2 for 25¢, or 6 for $1.10?

    Ⓐ 5 for $1.00
    Ⓑ 4 for 85¢
    Ⓒ 2 for 25¢
    Ⓓ 6 for $1.10

2. At grocery Store A, 5 cans of baked beans cost $3.45. At grocery Store B, 7 cans of baked beans cost $5.15. At grocery Store C, 4 cans of baked beans cost $2.46. At grocery Store D, 6 cans of baked beans cost $4.00. How much money would you save if you bought 20 cans of baked beans from grocery store C than if you bought 20 cans of baked beans from grocery store A?

    Ⓐ $1.75
    Ⓑ $1.25
    Ⓒ $1.50
    Ⓓ 95¢

3. Beverly drove from Atlantic City to Newark. She drove for 284 miles at a constant speed of 58 mph. How long did it take Beverly to complete the trip?

    Ⓐ 4 hours and 45 minutes
    Ⓑ 4 hours and 54 minutes
    Ⓒ 4 hours and 8 minutes
    Ⓓ 4 hours and 89 minutes

4. Don has two jobs. For Job 1, he earns $7.55 an hour. For Job 2, he earns $8.45 an hour. Last week he worked at the first job for 10 hours and at the second job for 15 hours. What were his average earnings per hour?

    Ⓐ $8.00
    Ⓑ $8.09
    Ⓒ $8.15
    Ⓓ $8.13

5. It took Marjorie 15 minutes to drive from her house to her daughter's school. If the school was 4 miles away from her house, what was her unit rate of speed? Express your answer in mph

[ ]

6. The Belmont race track known as "Big Sandy" is 1½ miles long. In 1973, Secretariat won the Belmont Stakes race in 2 minutes and 30 seconds. Assuming he ran on "Big Sandy", what was his unit speed?

    Ⓐ 30 mph
    Ⓑ 40 mph
    Ⓒ 36 mph
    Ⓓ 38 mph

7. If 1 pound of chocolate creams at Philadelphia Candies costs $7.52. How much does that candy cost by the ounce?

    Ⓐ 48¢ per oz.
    Ⓑ 47¢ per oz.
    Ⓒ 75.2¢ per oz.
    Ⓓ 66¢ per oz.

8. If Carol pays $62.90 to fill the 17-gallon gas tank in her vehicle and she can drive 330 miles on one tank of gas, about how much does she pay per mile to drive her vehicle?

[ ]

9. A 13 ounce box of cereal costs $3.99. What is the unit price per pound?

    Ⓐ about $1.23
    Ⓑ about $2.66
    Ⓒ about $4.30
    Ⓓ about $4.91

10. A bottle of perfume costs $26.00 for a $\frac{1}{2}$ ounce bottle. What is the price per ounce?

[ ]

Chapter 1

Lesson 8: Represent benchmark fractions and percents

1. **What fraction does the number line show**

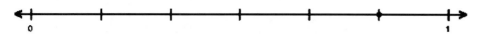

- Ⓐ $\frac{4}{6}$
- Ⓑ $\frac{5}{6}$
- Ⓒ $\frac{3}{6}$
- Ⓓ $\frac{1}{6}$

2. **What fraction does the number line show?**

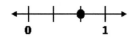

- Ⓐ $\frac{2}{3}$
- Ⓑ $\frac{1}{3}$
- Ⓒ $\frac{3}{3}$
- Ⓓ $\frac{4}{3}$

3. **What fraction does the number line show?**

Ⓐ $\dfrac{1}{4}$

Ⓑ $\dfrac{2}{4}$

Ⓒ $\dfrac{3}{4}$

Ⓓ $\dfrac{4}{4}$

4. **What fraction does the number line show?**

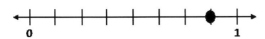

Ⓐ $\dfrac{8}{9}$

Ⓑ $\dfrac{7}{8}$

Ⓒ $\dfrac{2}{8}$

Ⓓ $\dfrac{5}{9}$

5. **What fraction does the number line show?**

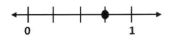

Ⓐ $\dfrac{1}{4}$

Ⓑ $\dfrac{3}{3}$

Ⓒ $\dfrac{2}{4}$

Ⓓ $\dfrac{3}{4}$

6. **What fraction does the number line show?**

0   1

Ⓐ $\dfrac{7}{8}$

Ⓑ $\dfrac{6}{8}$

Ⓒ $\dfrac{5}{8}$

Ⓓ $\dfrac{5}{3}$

7. **Which fractions does the number line show? Select all correct answers.**

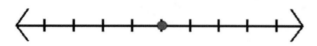

0   1

Ⓐ $\dfrac{3}{7}$

Ⓑ $\dfrac{1}{4}$

Ⓒ $\dfrac{4}{8}$

Ⓓ $\dfrac{1}{2}$

8. **What fraction does the number line show? Write your answer in the box below. Do not write in the most simplified form.**

0   1

9. Which point on the number line represents 3/5? Choose the correct answer.

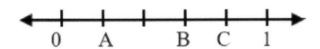

Ⓐ A
Ⓑ B
Ⓒ C

10. What fraction does the dot marked on the number line indicate? Choose the correct answer.

Ⓐ $\frac{1}{3}$

Ⓑ $\frac{2}{3}$

Ⓒ $\frac{3}{3}$

Ⓓ $\frac{3}{4}$

Chapter 1

Lesson 9: Applying Ratios and Percents

1. What value of x will make these two expressions equivalent?

    $\dfrac{-3}{7}$ and $\dfrac{x}{21}$

2. If p varies proportionally to s, and p = 10 when s = 2, which of the following equations correctly models this relationship? Select all the correct answers.

    Ⓐ p = 5s
    Ⓑ p = 10s
    Ⓒ s = 10p
    Ⓓ 10s = 2p

3. Solve for x, if $\dfrac{72}{108}$ and $\dfrac{x}{54}$ are equivalent.

4. At one particular store, the sale price, s, is always 75% of the displayed price, d. Which of the following equations correctly shows how to calculate s from d?

    Ⓐ d = 75s
    Ⓑ s = 0.75d
    Ⓒ s = d - 0.75
    Ⓓ s = d + 75

5. When x = 6, y = 4. If y is proportional to x, what is the value for y when x = 9?

 Ⓐ 4

 Ⓑ $\dfrac{2}{3}$

 Ⓒ 3
 Ⓓ 6

6. Jim is shopping for a suit to wear to his friend's wedding. He finds the perfect one on sale at 30% off. If the original price was $250.00, what will the selling price be after the discount?

 Ⓐ $75
 Ⓑ $175
 Ⓒ $200
 Ⓓ $220

7. If Julie bought her prom dress on sale at 15% off and paid $110.49 before tax, find the original price of her dress.

 Ⓐ $126.55
 Ⓑ $129.99
 Ⓒ $135.00
 Ⓓ $139.99

8. A plot of land is listed for sale with the following measurements: 1300 ft x 982 ft. When the buyer measured the land, he found that it measured 1285 ft by 982 ft. What was the % of error of the area of the plot?

 Ⓐ 1.47%
 Ⓑ 14.73%
 Ⓒ 1.15%
 Ⓓ 11.7%

9. Pierre received a parking ticket whose cost is $22.00. Each month that he failed to make payment, fees of $7.00 were added. By the time he paid the ticket, his bill was $36.00. What was the ratio of fees to the cost of the ticket?

Ⓐ $\dfrac{36}{22}$

Ⓑ $\dfrac{22}{36}$

Ⓒ $\dfrac{7}{22}$

Ⓓ $\dfrac{7}{11}$

10. Sara owns a used furniture store. She bought a chest for $42 and sold it for $73.50. What percent did she mark up the chest?

Ⓐ 100%
Ⓑ 75%
Ⓒ 42%
Ⓓ 31.5%

Chapter 1

Lesson 10: Equivalency

1. Reduce the fraction $\frac{44}{99}$ to its lowest terms:

   Ⓐ $\frac{1}{5}$

   Ⓑ $\frac{3}{7}$

   Ⓒ $\frac{2}{7}$

   Ⓓ $\frac{4}{9}$

2. Patrick climbed $\frac{4}{5}$ of the way up the trunk of a tree. Jacob climbed $\frac{80}{100}$ of the way up the same tree. To accomplish the same distance as Patrick and Jacob, how far up that tree trunk will Devon have to climb?

   Ⓐ $\frac{15}{20}$

   Ⓑ $\frac{60}{75}$

   Ⓒ $\frac{100}{200}$

   Ⓓ $\frac{28}{42}$

3. The cheerleaders ate $\frac{9}{18}$ of a sheet cake. Write this fraction in lowest terms.

   Ⓐ $\frac{1}{9}$

   Ⓑ $\frac{1}{2}$

   Ⓒ $\frac{2}{3}$

   Ⓓ $\frac{3}{6}$

4. Which group of fractions can all be reduced to $\frac{2}{9}$?

   Ⓐ $\frac{23}{27}$, $\frac{4}{36}$, $\frac{30}{270}$

   Ⓑ $\frac{25}{50}$, $\frac{30}{60}$, $\frac{50}{100}$

   Ⓒ $\frac{4}{18}$, $\frac{6}{27}$, $\frac{50}{225}$

   Ⓓ $\frac{6}{21}$, $\frac{20}{70}$, $\frac{36}{84}$

5. What do these fractions have in common?

$$\frac{10}{16}, \frac{15}{24}, \frac{20}{32}, \frac{25}{40}, \frac{30}{48}$$

(A) These fractions are equivalent to $\frac{5}{9}$

(B) These fractions are equivalent to $\frac{5}{8}$

(C) These fractions are equivalent to $\frac{10}{12}$

(D) These fractions are equivalent to $\frac{4}{8}$

6. Write the simplest form of $\frac{120}{150}$. Write the answer in the box given below.

7. Choose the fractions that can be simplified to $\frac{1}{2}$? Select all the correct answer.

(A) $\frac{24}{26}$

(B) $\frac{2}{4}$

(C) $\frac{5}{11}$

(D) $\frac{35}{70}$

(E) $\frac{9}{20}$

(F) $\frac{7}{14}$

8. Which group of fractions are equivalent to $\frac{4}{12}$? Select all the correct answers.

(A) $\frac{1}{3}, \frac{2}{5}, \frac{3}{9}$

(B) $\frac{1}{3}, \frac{2}{6}, \frac{3}{9}$

(C) $\frac{1}{3}, \frac{2}{5}, \frac{5}{20}$

(D) $\frac{6}{18}, \frac{12}{36}, \frac{15}{45}$

9. Fill in the missing number; $\frac{3}{5} = \frac{72}{?}$

    Ⓐ 120
    Ⓑ 125
    Ⓒ 122
    Ⓓ 124

10. The area model below represents $\frac{1}{4}$.

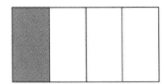

It has been decomposed into smaller units by drawing two dashed lines.

What is the equivalent fraction represented by the area model? Choose the correct option

  Ⓐ $\frac{3}{4}$

  Ⓑ $\frac{1}{12}$

  Ⓒ $\frac{3}{12}$

  Ⓓ $\frac{5}{12}$

Chapter 1

Lesson 11: Factors and Multiples

1. **Which of these statements is true of the number 17?**

   Ⓐ It is a factor of 17.
   Ⓑ It is a multiple of 17.
   Ⓒ It is prime.
   Ⓓ All of the above are true.

2. **What are the single digit prime numbers?**

   Ⓐ 2, 3, 5, and 7
   Ⓑ 1, 2, 3, 5, and 7
   Ⓒ 3, 5, and 7
   Ⓓ 1, 3, 5, and 7

3. **Which of the following sets below contains only prime numbers?**

   Ⓐ 7, 11, 49
   Ⓑ 7, 37, 51
   Ⓒ 7, 23, 47
   Ⓓ 2, 29, 93

4. **The product of three numbers is equal to 105. If the first two numbers are 7 and 5, what is the third number?**

   Ⓐ 35
   Ⓑ 7
   Ⓒ 5
   Ⓓ 3

5. **What is the prime factorization of 240?**

   Ⓐ $2 \times 2 \times 2 \times 5$
   Ⓑ $2 \times 2 \times 2 \times 2 \times 15$
   Ⓒ $2 \times 2 \times 2 \times 2 \times 5 \times 3$
   Ⓓ $2 \times 2 \times 2 \times 5 \times 3$

6. Office A's building complex and the school building next door have the same number of rooms. Office A's building complex has floors with 5 one-room offices on each, and the school building has 11 classrooms on each floor. What is the fewest number of rooms that each building can have?

Ⓐ 16
Ⓑ 6
Ⓒ 55
Ⓓ $\frac{5}{11}$

7. How do you know if a number is divisible by 3?

Ⓐ if the ones digit is an even number
Ⓑ if the ones digit is 0 or 5
Ⓒ if the sum of the digits in the number is divisible by 3 or a multiple of 3
Ⓓ if the sum of the digits in the number is divisible by 2 and 3

8. Find the Greatest Common Factor (GCF) for 42 and 56.

9. What is the prime factorization of 110?

10. What is the LCM of 16 and 24?

Chapter 1

Lesson 12: Equations and Expressions

1. When the expression 3(n + 7) is evaluated for a given value of n, the result is 33. What is the value of n?

    Ⓐ n = 4
    Ⓑ n = 5
    Ⓒ n = 21
    Ⓓ n = 120

2. Which number is acting as a coefficient in this expression? 360 + 22x − 448

    Ⓐ 360
    Ⓑ 22
    Ⓒ 448
    Ⓓ None of these

3. Evaluate the following when n = 7: 5(n − 5)

    Ⓐ 10
    Ⓑ −60
    Ⓒ 60
    Ⓓ 30

4. For which of the following values of b does the expression 4b − 9 have a value between 90 and 100?

    Ⓐ b = 104
    Ⓑ b = 26
    Ⓒ b = 48
    Ⓓ b = 24

5. Evaluate the following when n = −4: [5n − 3n] + 2n

    Ⓐ n = 16
    Ⓑ n = −20
    Ⓒ n = −16
    Ⓓ n = 0

6. Translate the following: "Four times a number n is equal to the difference between that number and 10"

   Ⓐ   4n = 10 − n
   Ⓑ   4 + n = 10*n
   Ⓒ   4/n = n + 10
   Ⓓ   4n = n − 10

7. Evaluate 2y + 3y − y when y = 2.

8. Find the value of 2b − 4 + 6y when b = 2 and y = 3.

9. Translate the following, and then solve: "A number n times 16 is equal to 48."

   Ⓐ   16n = 48, n = 4
   Ⓑ   16n = 48, n = 8
   Ⓒ   16 + n = 48, n = 32
   Ⓓ   16n = 48, n = 3

10. For which value of x does 6x + 12 evaluate to 54?

Chapter 1

Lesson 13: Identifying Equivalent Expressions

1. **Which two expressions are equivalent?**

   Ⓐ $(\frac{5}{25})x$ and $(\frac{1}{3})x$

   Ⓑ $(\frac{5}{25})x$ and $(\frac{1}{5})x$

   Ⓒ $(\frac{5}{25})x$ and $(\frac{1}{4})x$

   Ⓓ $(\frac{5}{25})x$ and $(\frac{1}{6})x$

2. **Which two expressions are equivalent? Select all the answers.**

   Ⓐ $7 + 21v$ and $2(5 + 3v)$
   Ⓑ $7 + 21v$ and $3(4 + 7v)$
   Ⓒ $7 + 21v$ and $7(1 + 3v)$
   Ⓓ $7 + 21v$ and $21(\frac{1}{3} + v)$

3. **Which two expressions are equivalent?**

   Ⓐ $\frac{32p}{2}$ and $17p$

   Ⓑ $\frac{32p}{2}$ and $18p$

   Ⓒ $\frac{32p}{2}$ and $16p$

   Ⓓ $\frac{32p}{2}$ and $14p$

4. **Which two expressions are equivalent?**

   Ⓐ $17(3m + 4)$ and $51m + 68$
   Ⓑ $17(3m + 4)$ and $51m + 67$
   Ⓒ $17(3m + 4)$ and $51m - 68$
   Ⓓ $17(3m + 4)$ and $47m + 51$

5. **Which two expressions are equivalent?**

   Ⓐ $\frac{64k}{4}$ and 4k

   Ⓑ $\frac{64k}{4}$ and 14k

   Ⓒ $\frac{64k}{4}$ and 16k

   Ⓓ $\frac{64k}{4}$ and 15k

6. **575d − 100 is equivalent to:**

   Ⓐ 25(23d − 4)
   Ⓑ 25(22d − 4)
   Ⓒ 25(23d + 4)
   Ⓓ 25(25d − 4)

7. **(800 + 444y)/4 is equivalent to:**

   Ⓐ 200 + 44y
   Ⓑ 800 + 111y
   Ⓒ 200 + 111y
   Ⓓ 200 − 111y

8. **5(19 −8y) is equivalent to:**

   Ⓐ 95 − 35y
   Ⓑ 95 + 40y
   Ⓒ 85 − 40y
   Ⓓ 95 − 40y

9. **The expression 3(26p − 7 + 14h) is equivalent to:**

   Ⓐ 78 − 21 + 42
   Ⓑ 78p + 21 + 42h
   Ⓒ 78p − 21 + 42
   Ⓓ 78p − 21 + 42h

10. **5(6x + 17y − 9z) is equivalent to:**

    Ⓐ 30x + 82y − 45z
    Ⓑ 20x + 85y − 40z
    Ⓒ 30x + 85y − 45z
    Ⓓ 30x − 85y + 45z

Chapter 1

Lesson 14: Formation of Expressions

1. Ruby is two years younger than her brother. If Ruby's brother's age is A, which of the following expressions correctly represents Ruby's age?

   Ⓐ A - 2
   Ⓑ A + 2
   Ⓒ 2A
   Ⓓ 2 - A

2. Find the difference:
   8n - (3n - 6)
   Write your answer in the box below.

3. Find the sum:
   6t + (3t - 5)
   Write your answer in the box below.

4. Combine like terms and factor the following expression.
   7x - 14x + 21x - 2
   Write your answer in the box below.

5. **Which of the following expressions is equivalent to:**

   3(x + 4) - 2

   Ⓐ 3x + 10
   Ⓑ 3x + 14
   Ⓒ 3x + 4
   Ⓓ 3x + 5

6. **Simplify the following expression:**

   $$(\frac{1}{2}) x + (\frac{3}{2}) x$$

   Ⓐ 2x

   Ⓑ $(\frac{5}{2}) x$

   Ⓒ - x

   Ⓓ $\frac{x}{2}$

7. **Simplify the following expression:**

   0.25x + 3 - 0.5x + 2

   Ⓐ -0.25x + 5
   Ⓑ 0.75x + 5
   Ⓒ -0.25x + 1
   Ⓓ 5.75x

8. **Which of the following statements correctly describes this expression?**

   2x + 4

   Ⓐ Four times a number plus two
   Ⓑ Two more than four times a number
   Ⓒ Four more than twice a number
   Ⓓ Twice a number less four

9. **Which of the following statements correctly describes the following expression?**

    $$\frac{2x - 3}{2}$$

    Ⓐ Half of three less than twice a number
    Ⓑ Half of twice a number
    Ⓒ Half of three less than a number
    Ⓓ Three less than twice a number

10. **Which of the following expressions is not equivalent to:**

    $$\left(\frac{1}{2}\right)(2x + 4) - 3$$

    Ⓐ $(x + 2) - 3$

    Ⓑ $\left(\dfrac{1}{2}\right)(2x + 4) - 3$

    Ⓒ $x - 1$

    Ⓓ $x + 1$

End of Numerical Representations and Relationships

Answer Key and Detailed Explanations

Chapter 1:
Numerical Representations and Relationships

Lesson 1: Classification of Numbers

Question No.	Answer	Detailed Explanations
1	A and C	An integer belongs to the set containing the counting numbers, their additive inverses, and zero. Therefore, (-3) and 7 are integers.
2	B	Rational numbers are the set of numbers that can be expressed as the quotient of two integers in which the denominator is not zero. All whole numbers can be expressed in this manner; so every whole number is a rational number.
3	B	$\sqrt{10}$ cannot be expressed as the ratio of two integers p and q and is therefore irrational.
4	B	Pi is the ratio of a circle's circumference to its diameter. It is therefore a real number. Pi cannot be expressed as the ratio of two integers, so it is irrational.
5	B	$\sqrt{7}$ cannot be expressed as the ratio of two integers and is therefore irrational. The irrationals are a subset of the real numbers.
6	D	The number 57 meets the requirements of each of the following sets of numbers: N (natural numbers), W (whole numbers), Z (integers), Q (rational numbers), and R (real numbers).
7	D	By definition, the natural numbers, N, are the set of counting numbers. Some mathematicians also include zero in this set. Since $\sqrt{16}$ = +4 or -4 and +4 is a counting number, it is included in N. None of the choices offered 0 as an option; so, in this case, it is a mute point.
8	B	3i is an imaginary number and therefore not rational and - $\sqrt{5.7}$ cannot be expressed as a terminating or repeating decimal and consequently is not rational. Therefore, there is only one choice that does not include one or the other or both of these two numbers. Option B is the correct answer.
9	B and D	$\sqrt{3}$ and $\sqrt{8}$ are non-terminating and non-repeating.
10	$\frac{15}{99}$	1- Write equation 1 - Assign the repeating rational number to x: x = 0.1515... 2- Write equation 2 - Multiply equation 1 by 100: 100x = 15.1515... 3- Subtract equation 1 from 2: 100x = 15.1515... x = 0.1515... 99x = 15 x = $\frac{15}{99}$

Lesson 2: Opposites & Absolute Values

Question No.	Answer	Detailed Explanations
1	D	Larissa has $4\frac{1}{2}$ cups of flour. Amount of flour needed to make cookies = $2\frac{3}{4}$ cups of flour. Amount of flour left after making cookies = $4\frac{1}{2} - 2\frac{3}{4}$ $4\frac{1}{2} - 2\frac{3}{4}$ = $\frac{9}{2} - \frac{11}{4} = \frac{9 \times 2}{2 \times 2} - \frac{11}{4} = \frac{18}{4} - \frac{11}{4} = \frac{18-11}{4} = \frac{7}{4} = 1\frac{3}{4}$
2	D	$\$2{,}123 - 2{,}400 = -\$277$ They must make a deposit of $277 in order to prevent the account from being overdrawn.
3	3	$1 + 4 - 2 = 3$
4	D	−4 is only 4 units away from 0 on a number line. All of the other numbers are farther away.
5	A	If you count the units between −5.5 and 7.5, you will count 13 units between them.
6	D	 The number line above shows −1, 3, and 4. All other answer choices are not represented on this number line.
7	B	$17 - \lvert(7)(-3)\rvert$ $= 17 - \lvert-21\rvert$ $= 17 - 21$ $= -4$ Note: Absolute value (the value of $\lvert x \rvert$) is the value of a number without regard to its sign.

Question No.	Answer	Detailed Explanations
8	A	$16 + \lvert(7)(-3) - 44\rvert - 5$ $= 16 + \lvert-21 - 44\rvert - 5$ $= 16 + \lvert-21 + (-44)\rvert - 5$ $= 16 + \lvert-65\rvert - 5$ $= 16 + 65 - 5$ $= 81 - 5$ $= 76$ Note: Absolute value (the value of $\lvert x\rvert$) is the value of a number without regard to its sign.
9	32	$\lvert15 - 47\rvert + 9 - \lvert(-2)(-4) - 17\rvert$ $= \lvert-32\rvert + 9 - \lvert8 - 17\rvert$ $= 32 + 9 - \lvert-9\rvert$ $= 32 + 9 - 9$ $= 41-9$ $= 32$ Note: Absolute value (the value of $\lvert x\rvert$) is the value of a number without regard to its sign.
10	64	$18 + 3\lvert6 - 25\rvert - 11$ $= 18 + 3\lvert-19\rvert - 11$ $= 18 + 3(19) - 11$ $= 18 + 57 - 11$ $= 18 + 57 - 11$ $= 75 - 11$ $= 64$ Note: Absolute value (the value of $\lvert x\rvert$) is the value of a number without regard to its sign.

Lesson 3: Using Number Lines

Question No.	Answer	Detailed Explanations
1	14	Distance between 9 and 16 = 7. Distance between two consecutive ticks = 7/7 = 1. Therefore the dot represents the number 14.
2	0	Distance between -5 and 3 = 8. Distance between two consecutive ticks = 8/8 = 1. Therefore the dot represents the number 0.
3	4	Distance between -2 and 14 = 16. Distance between two consecutive ticks = 16/8 = 2. Therefore the dot represents the number 4.
4	B	Distance between -10 and -6 = 4. Distance between two consecutive ticks = 4/8 = 0.5. Therefore the dot represents the number -7.5.
5	C	Distance between -25 and +25 = 50. Distance between two consecutive ticks = 50/10 = 5. Therefore the dot represents the number 5.
6	B	A negative account balance indicates a debt is owed. −$45 means $45 is owed. −$5 means $5 is owed. Therefore the account balance of −$45 represents the greatest debt.
7	A	The warmer temperatures are above zero. Of these two 5°F > 2°F . Therefore the warmest temperature is 5°F above zero.
8	A	First calculate the amount Anneliese spent: $58.00 + $35.00 = $93.00. If her account balance is −$142.00 then before she spent any money she had −$142.00 + $93.00 = −$49.00.
9	B	First calculate the elevation of the campground. They climbed to an elevation of 1839 feet and then descended 527 feet to the restaurant. So the restaurant is located at 1839 − 527 = 1312 feet. The campground is 264 feet higher than the restaurant and so is located at 1312 + 264 = 1576 feet. The difference in elevation between home and the campground is 1576 − 439 = 1137 feet.
10	C	Find the total debits and credits. Debits: (2*$5.99) + $28.00 = $39.98 Credits: $46.50 Now determine the account balance: $165.00 − $39.98 + $46.50 = $171.52

Lesson 4: Rational Numbers in Context

Question No.	Answer	Detailed Explanations
1	Xavier	−7 is greater than −12 so Xavier has the higher score.
2	A	Get a common denominator and compare fractions. The LCM between 6 and 12 is 12. Kelly: $\frac{(5 \times 2)}{(6 \times 2)} = \frac{10}{12}$ Helen: $\frac{9}{12}$ Kelly has read more because $\frac{10}{12} > \frac{9}{12}$ or $\frac{5}{6} > \frac{9}{12}$.
3	D	−52°F > −80°F −52°F is 52 degrees below zero whereas −80°F is 80 degrees below zero.
4	B	Rewrite these three numbers all as decimals or fractions. $1\frac{3}{4} = 1.75$ $\frac{20}{8} = 2.5$ 1.6 = 1.6 Now compare: 2.5 > 1.75 > 1.6 Now rewrite them in their original form: $\frac{20}{8} > 1\frac{3}{4} > 1.6$
5	D	−143 means 143 feet below sea level. −134 feet means 134 feet below sea level. Therefore Doug dove deeper because he went further below sea level than Sissy.
6	C	Rewrite these three numbers all as decimals or fractions. $\frac{4}{15} = 0.27$ 0.4 = 0.4 $\frac{1}{3} = 0.33$ Now compare: 0.4 > 0.33 > 0.27 Now rewrite them in their original form: $0.4 > \frac{1}{3} > \frac{4}{15}$

Question No.	Answer	Detailed Explanation
7	C	15 feet below sea level $= -15$ feet $\frac{33}{3} = 11$ feet below sea level $= -11$ feet 11.5 feet below sea level $= -11.5$ feet The deepest school is the one with the greater negative magnitude. Therefore: -15 is deeper than -11.5 is deeper than -11 or S1 > S3 > S2.
8	A	Get a common denominator and compare fractions. The LCM between 5 and 7 is 35. $\frac{(4 \times 7)}{(5 \times 7)} = \frac{28}{35}$ $\frac{(5 \times 5)}{(7 \times 5)} = \frac{25}{35}$ It snowed more on the first day because $\frac{28}{35} > \frac{25}{35}$ or $\frac{4}{5} > \frac{5}{7}$.
9	A and B	First determine the balance of Molly's account: $\$365 - \$415 = -\$50$ Molly has a balance of $-\$50$ so she owes the bank $\$50$. Bill has a balance of $-\$45$ so he owes the bank $\$45$. Therefore Molly owes the bank more than Bill.
10	B	Jeremiah has eaten $2\frac{5}{6}$ boxes. Farley has eaten $1\frac{15}{9} = 2\frac{6}{9}$ Since they both have eaten 2 boxes lets determine which is greater $\frac{5}{6}$ or $\frac{6}{9}$ The LCM of 6 and 9 is 18. $\frac{(5 \times 3)}{(6 \times 3)} = \frac{15}{18}$, $\frac{(6 \times 2)}{(9 \times 2)} = \frac{12}{18}$ Since $\frac{15}{18} > \frac{12}{18}$ Jeremiah has eaten more, therefore Farley has more left.

Lesson 5: Interpreting Fractions

Question No.	Answer	Detailed Explanations
1	A	The first three cookies can be shared by having each friend receive 1 whole cookie. That leaves 1 cookie to be divided among the three friends. This can be shown as a fraction with the dividend (1) as the numerator and the divisor (3) as the denominator. Each friend will receive 1 whole cookie and $\frac{1}{3}$ of the last cookie that was divided.
2	B	The number 5 goes into 18 three whole times (5 x 3 = 15), leaving a remainder of 3. That three can be divided by 5 to get the required fraction, $\frac{3}{5}$.
3	B	To solve, divide 90 minutes by 4 squads. This creates the improper fraction $\frac{90}{4}$. To change it to a mixed number, divide 90 by 4 to get 22 remainder 2. The remainder of 2 also needs to be divided among the 4 squads, so it becomes the fraction $\frac{2}{4}$, or $\frac{1}{2}$. Each squad will play for $22\frac{1}{2}$ minutes.
4	D	To find $\frac{2}{5}$ of 695, multiply the whole number by the fraction. Since $\frac{2}{5}$ is really 2 ÷ 5, this means you will multiply 695 x 2 ÷ 5.
5	C	7 hours divided by 5 people is the fraction $\frac{7}{5}$. Of this, $\frac{5}{5}$ equals one whole, leaving $\frac{2}{5}$ as a fraction. These $\frac{2}{5}$ are not 2 minutes, they are a fraction of an hour. The total time is $1\frac{2}{5}$.
6	D	A fraction is the division of the numerator by the denominator. The fraction $\frac{3}{10}$ is equivalent to 3 ÷ 10.
7	C	A fraction is the division of the numerator by the denominator.
8	$\frac{1}{9}$	The division of two whole numbers (such as 1 cake divided by 9 people) can be shown as a fraction with the dividend as the numerator and the divisor as the denominator.
9	4	A fraction is the division of the numerator by the denominator. The fraction $\frac{4}{7}$ is equivalent to 4÷7. Therefore, $\frac{4}{7}$ x 7= $\frac{4 \times 7}{7}$ = $\frac{28}{7}$ = 4.
10	2	A fraction is the division of the numerator by the denominator. The fraction $\frac{2}{3}$ is equivalent to 2 ÷ 3.

Lesson 6: Expressing Ratios

Question No.	Answer	Detailed Explanations
1	C	First, to find the proper ratio, subtract the number of girls from the total number of students. The difference is the number of boys. $600-330 = 270$. So, the initial ratio is $\frac{270}{600}$. Then, to rewrite a ratio in its simplest terms, divide the numerator and denominator by the Greatest Common Factor (GCF). Here, the GCF is 30. 270 divided by 30 = 9 and 600 divided by 30 = 20, so, the simplest ratio is $\frac{9}{20}$.
2	D	First, find the ratio of emeralds to rubies. That ratio is $\frac{85}{119}$. To find how many pearls the sultan had, set up a proportion with the ratio of diamonds to pearls: $\frac{85}{119} = \frac{45}{x}$ Then, find the cross products of each: $85*x = 119*45$ Simplify: $85x = 5355$ Solve for x by dividing by 85 on both sides: $\frac{85x}{85} = \frac{5355}{85}$ $x = 63$
3	B	$75 + 125 = 200$. Therefore, the total number of birds is 200. The ratio of geese to total birds is 75:200. Simplify the ratio by dividing by the GCF (75,200)= 25, simplified ratio is 3:8.
4	D	There are $(7+5+2) = 14$ players in all. The ratio of redheads to the team is 2:14. Divide by the GCF of 2 to simplify the ratio to 1:7
5	C	Set up the proportion: $\frac{2}{14}=\frac{x}{126}$, $\frac{1}{7}=\frac{x}{126}$, cross multiply to get $7x = 126$, then divide by 7 and $x = 18$.
6	D	The total number of birds is $175+63 = 238$. Thus, the ratio of ducks to total birds is 175:238. To find the ratio in simplest terms, divide by the GCF(175, 238) =7. The ratio in simplest terms is 25:34.
7	A	The ratio of ducks to geese is 175:63. To find how many ducks, set up a proportion of $\frac{175}{63} = \frac{x}{4,725}$. Find the cross products: $175*4,725 = 63*x$ $826,875 = 63x$ Divide both sides by 63 $x = 13,125$

Question No.	Answer	Detailed Explanations
8	10	There are 3 teaspoons to each tablespoon. Thus $3 \times \frac{10}{3} = 10$ teaspoons.
9	44	To find how many students there are in the grade, set up the proportion $\frac{6}{5} = \frac{24}{x}$. Notice that you can multiply $\frac{6}{5}$ by $\frac{4}{4}$ to make the numerator of 24. This makes the equivalent denominator 20. Add 24 + 20 to get the total number of students, or 44.
10	18	If the ratio of pencils to pens is $\frac{3}{2}$ then the ratio of pencils to pencils and pens is $\frac{3}{5}$. To find the number of pencils in a box with 30 pencils and pens, set up the proportion $\frac{3}{5} = \frac{x}{30}$. Then, multiply the first ratio by $\frac{6}{6}$ which will equal $\frac{18}{30}$. There are 18 pencils in the box.

Lesson 7: Unit Rates

Question No.	Answer	Detailed Explanations
1	C	$\frac{1}{5}$ = a unit price of $0.20 per piece $\frac{.85}{4}$ = a unit price of $0.2125 per piece $\frac{.25}{2}$ = a unit price of $0.125 per piece. This is the best price per unit. $\frac{1.1}{6}$ = a unit price of $0.183 per piece.
2	C	The unit rate at Store A is $\frac{\$3.45}{5}$ = $0.69. 20 cans of beans would be $0.69*20= $13.80 The unit rate at Store C is $\frac{\$2.46}{4}$ = $0.615. 20 cans of beans would be $0.615*20=$12.30. Subtract $13.80−12.30=$1.50
3	B	284 miles divided by 58 miles per hour are how you will find how long it took Beverly to make the trip. (Distance ÷ rate = time) $\frac{284}{58}$ ≈ 4.9 hours 0.9 hours = 54 minutes (Multiply 60 by 0.9, because there are 60 minutes in an hour.) 4 hours and 54 minutes is how long it took Beverly to make the trip.
4	B	$7.55 x 10 = $75.55 $8.45 x 15 = $126.75 126.75 + 75.55 = 202.30 $\frac{202.30}{25}$ = $8.09
5	16 mph	$\frac{15}{4} = \frac{60}{x}$, where 60 equals the number of minutes in an hour. 15 x 4 = 60, so multiply the original ratio $\frac{15}{4}$ by $\frac{4}{4}$ to get $\frac{60}{16}$, where 16 represents the miles per hour (mph) that she traveled.
6	C	Set up a ratio of distance/time. Here, the ratio would be $\frac{1.5}{2.5}$ Then, create a proportion $\frac{1.5}{2.5} = \frac{x}{60}$, where 60 represents the number of minutes in an hour. Find the cross products: 1.5*60 = 2.5*x Simplify: 90 = 2.5x, Divide each side by 2.5 we get, x = 36.
7	B	There are 16 ounces in a pound, so $\frac{\$7.52}{16}$ = 47¢

Question No.	Answer	Detailed Explanations
8	$0.19	To find the cost of gas per mile: $\frac{\$62.90}{330}$ equals about $0.19 per mile. (Note: The capacity of the tank is extra information.)
9	D	$3.99/13 equals about $0.306 per ounce. Since there are 16 oz in a pound, multiply 16 by $0.306…, which equals about $4.91.
10	$52	$26.00 ÷ (1/2) = $26.00 x 2 = $52.00 per ounce

Lesson 8: Represent benchmark fractions and percents

Question No.	Answer	Detailed Explanations
1	B	The number line is divided into six segments and the dot is at the fifth segment of the six. The fraction is $\frac{5}{6}$.
2	A	The number line is divided into three segments and the dot is at the second segment of the three. The fraction is $\frac{2}{3}$.
3	B	The number line is divided into four segments and the dot is at the second segment of the four. The fraction is $\frac{2}{4}$.
4	B	The number line is divided into eight segments and the dot is at the seventh segment of the eight. The fraction is $\frac{7}{8}$.
5	D	The number line is divided into four segments and the dot is at the third segment of the four. The fraction is $\frac{3}{4}$.
6	C	The number line is divided into eight segments and the dot is at the fifth segment of the eight. The fraction is $\frac{5}{8}$.
7	C & D	The number line from 0 to 1 is divided into 8 equal segments. The number line is marked at the 4th segment. This represents $\frac{4}{8}$ of the whole line. $\frac{4}{8}$ can also be seen as $\frac{1}{2}$.
8	$\frac{4}{6}$	The number line from 0 to 1 is divided into 6 equal segments. The number line is marked at the 4th segment. This represents $\frac{4}{6}$ of the whole line.
9	B	The interval from 0 to 1 is taken as the whole and is divided into 5 equal segments. Each segment has a size 1/5. 3/5 is represented by the point located at the end of the 3rd segment from 0. In this problem, that point is B.
10	B	The number line from 0 to 1 is divided into 3 equal segments. The number line is marked at the 2nd segment. This represents 2/3 of the whole line.

Lesson 9: Applying Ratios and Percents

Question No.	Answer	Detailed Explanations
1	-9	In a set of equivalent ratios, or a proportion, the numerator and denominator of one ratio will be multiplied by the same number to get the values of the other ratio. In this case, the denominator of the first ratio, 7, is multiplied by 3 to get to 21. This means (-3) must also be multiplied by 3 to get to (-9).
2	A and D	To find the constant of proportionality, find the relationship between p and s. When p = 10 and s = 2, dividing p by s shows that p is 5 times s. Therefore, the equation that shows the constant of proportionality is p = 5s and 10s=2p.
3	36	To solve this proportion for x, multiply both sides of the equation by 54, and simplify the result, We get, x = 36.
4	B	To find the constant of proportionality, find the relationship between s and d. s is 75% of d, which is the same as 0.75 times d. Therefore, the equation that shows the constant of proportionality is s = 0.75d.
5	D	Set up a proportion between the known ratio and the unknown ratio, and solve for y. $\dfrac{6}{4} = \dfrac{9}{y}$ 6y = 9 (4) Cross Multiply 6y = 36 Simplify $\dfrac{6y}{6} = \dfrac{36}{6}$ Divide each side by 6 y = 6 Simplify
6	B	Selling price (sp) = Original price (op) - 0.30(op) sp = 250 - 0.30(250) sp = 250 - 75 sp = 175. $175 is the correct answer.
7	B	Original price (op) - 0.15(op) = Selling price (sp) op - 0.15(op) = 110.49 0.85(op) = 110.49 op $= \dfrac{110.49}{0.85}$ op = $129.99. $129.99 is the correct answer.

Question No.	Answer	Detailed Explanations
8	C	Using original measurements, Area=1300 x 982=1,276,600 sq ft. Using actual measurements, Area=1285 x 982=1,261,870 sq ft. Error = 14,730 sq ft. $\dfrac{14,730}{1,276,600} \times 100 = 1.15\%$ error. The correct answer is 1.15%. Alternate Explanation : Since width is same in both the cases, we can write error $=\dfrac{\text{(original length x width) - (measured length x width)}}{\text{(original length x width)}}$ $=\dfrac{(1300 \times 982) - (1285 \times 982)}{(1300 \times 982)} = 982$ $\dfrac{1300 - 1285}{1300 \times 982}$. Since 982 is common factor in both numerator and denominator, error $=\dfrac{1300 - 1285}{1300} = \dfrac{15}{1300} = 0.0115 = 1.15\%$
9	D	$36.00 - $22.00 = $14.00 in fees. $\dfrac{\$14.00}{\$22.00} = \dfrac{14}{22} = \dfrac{7}{11}$ is the ratio of fees to the cost of the ticket. $\dfrac{7}{11}$ is the correct answer.
10	B	Selling price - cost = markup $73.50 - $42.00 = $31.50 markup Mark up/ cost = percent of mark up $\dfrac{\$31.50}{\$42} = 0.75 = 75\%$ markup. The correct answer is 75%.

Lesson 10: Equivalency

Question No.	Answer	Detailed Explanations
1	D	Find the GCF, which is the largest factor that both the numerator and denominator can be divided by.
2	B	The correct fraction can be reduced to its lowest terms of $\frac{4}{5}$: Find the Greatest Common Factor (GCF), which is a number that the numerator and denominator can be divided by: 80 divided by 20 = 4 and 100 divided by 20 = 5. In this case, the GCF is 20. The number of times the numerator and denominator divides evenly into the GCF ($\frac{4}{5}$) is the lowest terms. $\frac{60}{75}$ also reduces to $\frac{4}{5}$ when reduced to lowest terms. (GCF = 15)
3	B	Reduce the fraction to its lowest terms by dividing the numerator and denominator by the GCF (9).
4	C	Use the GCF of the numerator and denominator of each fraction to determine if it is equivalent to $\frac{2}{9}$.
5	B	These fractions all reduce to $\frac{5}{8}$ in their lowest terms.
6	4/5	30 is the GCF of 120 and 150. When the GCF is taken out from both the numerator and denominator, 120/150 reduces to 4/5.
7	B,D,F	Divide out common terms as much as you can. Once you cannot simplify anymore, see which fractions are equivalent to $\frac{1}{2}$. $$\frac{2}{4} = \frac{\frac{1}{2}}{\frac{4}{2}} = \frac{1}{2}$$ $$\frac{35}{70} = \frac{\frac{35}{35}}{\frac{7}{35}} = \frac{1}{2}$$ $$\frac{7}{14} = \frac{\frac{7}{7}}{\frac{14}{7}} = \frac{1}{2}$$ Therefore, $\frac{2}{4}$, $\frac{35}{70}$ and $\frac{7}{14}$ are equivalent to $\frac{1}{2}$

Question No.	Answer	Detailed Explanations
8	B & D	$\frac{1}{3} = \frac{1 \times 2}{3 \times 2} = \frac{2}{6}$; $\frac{1}{3} = \frac{1 \times 3}{3 \times 3} = \frac{3}{9}$; Therefore, option (B) is correct. $\frac{1}{3} = \frac{1 \times 6}{3 \times 6} = \frac{6}{18}$; $\frac{1}{3} = \frac{1 \times 12}{3 \times 12} = \frac{12}{36}$; $\frac{1}{3} = \frac{1 \times 15}{3 \times 15} = \frac{15}{45}$ Therefore, option (D) is correct.
9	A	We get an equivalent fraction of a fraction by multiplying both the numerator and the denominator by the same number. In this problem, the numerators are 3 and 72. What is the number, when multiplied by 3 gives 72? It is 24. Therefore, we multiply the denominator (5) by 24 to get the missing number; 5 x 24 = 120.
10	C	After decomposing into smaller units, the whole is divided into 3 shaded parts and 12 total number of parts. Therefore, the fraction represented by the figure is . So, $\frac{1}{4} = \frac{3}{12}$ $\frac{1}{12}$ When we multiply both the numerator and the denominator of a fraction by the same number, we get an equivalent fraction. $\frac{1}{4} = \frac{(1 \times 3)}{(4 \times 3)} . =$

Lesson 11: Factors and Multiples

Question No.	Answer	Detailed Explanations
1	D	All statements are true. A number is always a factor and a multiple of itself. It is prime because the only two factors are 1 and 17.
2	A	Other than 1, which is not prime by definition, 2, 3, 5, and 7 are the only single-digit numbers that can be divided by only themselves and 1.
3	C	A prime number is a whole number (greater than 1) which is divisible by only 1 and itself. The set {7, 23, 47} contains three numbers which fit the definition stated above. Each number is divisible by only 1 and itself.
4	D	(7*5) * x = 105 35x = 105 x = 3
5	C	The prime factorization of a number are the prime numbers that when multiplied together, give a product of the starting number. 240 = 120 x 2 120 = 60 x 2 60 = 30 x 2 30 = 15 x 2 15 = 5 x 3 2 x 2 x 2 x 2 x 3 x 5 = 240
6	C	Find the least multiple common to both numbers, starting with the greater number: 11: 11, 22, 33, 44, 55, 66, 77, 88... 5: 5, 10, 15, 20, 25, 30, 35, 40, 45, 50, 55 Stop when you get to the lowest multiple that is common to both. 55 is the LCM (lowest common multiple) of these two numbers, so each building could have 55 rooms.
7	C	When the sum of the digits in the number equals three or a multiple of 3, the number is divisible by 3. For example, 375 is divisible by 3 because 3 + 7 + 5 = 15 Because 15 is a multiple of 3, the number is divisible by 3.

Question No.	Answer	Detailed Explanations
8	14	42: 1, 2, 3, 6, 7, 14, 21, 42 56: 1, 2, 4, 7, 8, 14, 28, 56 The greatest common factor is 14.
9	2 × 5 × 11	Prime factorization is when a number is factored as far as possible into its prime factors. Start by factoring a number into two factors: 110 can be factored into two factors of 11 X 10. 11 is a prime number, so that is the first prime factor. 10 is composite so it can be factored into factors of 2 and 5. 2 and 5 are both prime numbers, so those are the remaining prime factors. Thus, the prime factorization of 110 is 2 X 5 X 11
10	48	To find the LCM, list the first few multiples of each number: 16: 16, 32, 48, 64 24: 24, 48, 72 48 is the least multiple that is common to both lists.

Lesson 12: Equations and Expressions

Question No.	Answer	Detailed Explanations
1	A	Since 3(n + 7) is equal to 33, then (n + 7) must equal 11 (3 x 11 = 33). Therefore, n must equal 4, since 4 + 7 = 11.
2	B	A number joined to a variable through multiplication is a coefficient. 22 is the coefficient of x.
3	A	When n = 7, the expression becomes 5(7 - 5) = 5 (2) = 10.
4	B	When b = 26, 4b − 9 = 4(26) − 9 = 104 − 9 = 95
5	C	When n = −4, the expression becomes: = [5(-4) − 3(-4)] + 2(-4) = [−20 − (−12)] − 8 = [−20 + 12] − 8 = [−8] − 8 = −16 Alternative Solution: [5n-3n]+2n = 2n + 2n = 4n = 4*(-4) = -16
6	D	Four times a number n means to multiply the variable n by 4, 4n. is equal to means = the difference between a number and 10 means to write the subtraction as is, from left to right, so n − 10. Therefore, 4n = n − 10
7	8	First, combine like terms: 2y + 3y − y = 4y Then, substitute 2 for y: 4(2) =8
8	18	Substitute 2 for b and 3 for y: 2(2) − 4 + 6(3) = 4 − 4 + 18 = 0 + 18 = 18
9	D	a number n times 16 is equal to 48 a number n times 16: 16n is equal to: = 16n = 48 n = 3, since 16(3) = 48
10	54	When x = 7, 6x + 12 = 6(7) + 12 = 42 + 12 = 54

Lesson 13: Identifying Equivalent Expressions

Question No.	Answer	Detailed Explanation
1	B	$(\frac{5}{25})x$ and $(\frac{1}{5})x$ are equivalent because $\frac{5}{25}$ simplifies to $\frac{1}{5}$. The expressions will be equivalent even if a number is substituted for x.
2	C and D	7 + 21v and 7(1 + 3v) are equivalent because if you distribute 7 to 1 + 3v you will get 7 + 21v. Similarly, 7 + 21v and 21($\frac{1}{3}$ + v) are also equivalent. The expressions will be equivalent even if a number is substituted for v.
3	C	32p/2 and 16p are equivalent because if you divide 32p by 2 you get 16p. The expressions will be equivalent even if a number is substituted for p.
4	A	17(3m + 4) and 51m + 68 are equivalent because if you distribute 17 to 3m + 4 you will get 51m + 68. The expressions will be equivalent even if a number is substituted for m.
5	C	64k/4 and 16k are equivalent because if you divide 64k by 4 you will get 16k. The expressions will be equivalent even if a number is substituted for k.
6	A	25(23d − 4) and 575d − 100 are equivalent because if you distribute 25 to 23d − 4 you will get 575d − 100. The expressions will be equivalent even if a number is substituted for d.
7	C	(800 + 444y)/4 and 200 + 111y are equivalent because if you divide 800 + 444y by 4 you will get 200 + 111y. The expressions will be equivalent even if a number is substituted for y.
8	D	5(19 − 8y) and 95 − 40y are equivalent because if you distribute 5 to 19 − 8y you will get 95 − 40y. The expressions will be equivalent even if a number is substituted for y.
9	D	3(26p − 7 + 14h) and 78p − 21 + 42h are equivalent because if you distribute 3 to 26p − 7 + 14h you will get 78p − 21 + 42h. The expressions will be equivalent even if numbers are substituted for h and p.
10	C	5(6x + 17y − 9z) and 30x + 85y − 45z are equivalent because if you distribute 5 to 6x + 17y − 9z you will get 30x + 85y − 45z. The expressions will be equivalent even if x, y, and z are replaced with numbers.

Lesson 14: Formation of Expressions

Question No.	Answer	Detailed Explanations
1	A	Remember: "Younger than" is a key phrase that will indicate subtraction. If A is the age of Ruby's brother, and she is 2 years younger than her brother. The correct expression is A - 2.
2	5n+6	8n - (3n-6) = 8n - 3n + 6 = 5n + 6. 5n + 6 is the correct answer.
3	9t - 5	6t + (3t - 5) = Remove parentheses: 6t + (3t − 5) = 6t + 3t - 5. Now combine like terms: 6t + 3t − 5 = 9t − 5. 9t - 5 is the correct answer.
4	2(7x - 1)	7x - 14x + 21x - 2. Here, I will combine like terms first. 7x - 14x + 21x = 14x. Now we have 14x − 2, which factors into 2(7x - 1). 2(7x - 1) is the correct answer.

5	A	Simplify the expression 3(x + 4) - 2
		Step 1: Multiply terms in parentheses by 3
		    3x+12-2
		Step 2: Combine like terms
		    3x+10

6	A	Simplify the expression $(\frac{1}{2})x + (\frac{3}{2})x$ Add the numerators of the fractions and keep the same denominators $(\frac{4}{2})x$ Simplify this fraction we get 2x.
7	A	Simplify the expression 0.25x + 3 - 0.5x + 2 by combining like terms Step 1: 0.25x - 0.5x + 3 + 2 Step 2: -0.25x + 5
8	C	Remember: Addition means more than and 2x represents multiplication, or times. The statement that represents the expression 2x + 4 is four more than two times a number.

Question No.	Answer	Detailed Explanations
9	A	Remember: A half can be represented by the fraction $\frac{1}{2}$, twice indicates multiplication, and less represents subtraction. Considering the numerator (2x-3), means 3 less than twice a number 'x'. Dividing this by half, we get half of three less than twice a number.
10	D	Simplify the expression $\frac{1}{2}$ (2x + 4) - 3 Step 1: Multiply terms in parentheses by $\frac{1}{2}$ (x+2) - 3 Step 2: Combine like terms (x - 1)

Chapter 2

Computations and Algebraic Relationships

Chapter 2

Lesson 1: Division of Fractions

1. **What is the quotient of 20 divided by one-fourth?**

2. **Calculate:** $1\dfrac{1}{2} \div \dfrac{3}{4} =$

   Ⓐ 4

   Ⓑ $\dfrac{1}{2}$

   Ⓒ $\dfrac{3}{4}$

   Ⓓ 2

3. **Calculate:** $3\dfrac{2}{3} \div 2\dfrac{1}{6} =$

   Ⓐ $\dfrac{8}{13}$

   Ⓑ $\dfrac{12}{13}$

   Ⓒ $1\dfrac{5}{13}$

   Ⓓ $1\dfrac{9}{13}$

4. Calculate: $2\dfrac{3}{4} \div \dfrac{11}{4} =$

    (A) 1
    (B) 2
    (C) 3
    (D) 4

5. Calculate: $\dfrac{7}{8} \div \dfrac{3}{4} =$

    (A) $1\dfrac{1}{6}$

    (B) 2

    (C) $\dfrac{21}{32}$

    (D) $\dfrac{5}{9}$

6. Calculate: $6\dfrac{3}{4} \div 1\dfrac{1}{8} =$

    (A) $\dfrac{1}{6}$

    (B) 4

    (C) $5\dfrac{3}{4}$

    (D) 6

7. Complete the following division using mental math.

    7 divided by $\dfrac{1}{5}$

8. Complete the following division using mental math.

11 divided by $\dfrac{6}{6}$

9. What is the result when a fraction is multiplied by its reciprocal?

Ⓐ $\dfrac{1}{2}$

Ⓑ 10

Ⓒ 1

Ⓓ It cannot be determined.

10. Simplify the following problem. Do not solve.

$$\dfrac{14}{21} \div \dfrac{28}{7}$$

Ⓐ $\dfrac{14}{21} \div \dfrac{28}{7}$

Ⓑ $\dfrac{2}{3} \times \dfrac{1}{4}$

Ⓒ 1

Ⓓ 10

Chapter 2

Lesson 2: Numbers multiplied by fractions

1. **Which statement is true about the following equation?**
   $$6,827 \times \frac{2}{7} = ?$$

   Ⓐ The product will be less than 6,827.
   Ⓑ The product will be greater than 6,827.
   Ⓒ The product will be less than $\frac{2}{7}$.
   Ⓓ The product will be equal to 6,827 ÷ 7.

2. **Which statement is true about the following equation?**
   $$27,093 \times \frac{5}{4} = ?$$

   Ⓐ The product will be equal to 27,093 ÷ 54.
   Ⓑ The product will be less than $\frac{5}{4}$.
   Ⓒ The product will be less than 27,093.
   Ⓓ The product will be greater than 27,093.

3. **Estimate the product:**
   $$18,612 \times 1\frac{1}{7} = ?$$

   Ⓐ 15,000
   Ⓑ 21,000
   Ⓒ 38,000
   Ⓓ 2,500

4. **Which number completes the equation?**
   $$3,606 \times \underline{\quad} = 4,808$$

   Ⓐ $\frac{2}{3}$

   Ⓑ $\frac{4}{3}$

   Ⓒ $2\frac{1}{2}$

   Ⓓ $\frac{9}{3}$

5. Which number completes the equation?

$$\_\_\_ \times \frac{5}{6} = 17{,}365$$

Ⓐ 5,838
Ⓑ 50,838
Ⓒ 20,838
Ⓓ 10,838

6. When 6 is multiplied by the following fractions, which of the products will be greater than 6? Select all the correct answers.

Ⓐ $\frac{4}{5}$

Ⓑ $\frac{10}{9}$

Ⓒ $\frac{3}{2}$

Ⓓ $\frac{13}{14}$

7. Write the correct comparison symbol that best completes the statement.

Ⓐ $5 \times \frac{2}{3} \square 5$

Ⓑ $\frac{4}{3} \times 8 \square 8$

Ⓒ $12 \times \frac{4}{7} \square 12$

Ⓓ $4 \times \frac{24}{24} \square 4$

8. Which of the following expressions is true.

Ⓐ $25 \times \frac{6}{7} > 25$

Ⓑ $\frac{4}{3} \times 43 < 43$

Ⓒ $\frac{9}{15} \times 16 < 16$

Ⓓ $59 \times \frac{19}{20} > 59$

9. Compare using < , > or =

$$44 \;\square\; 44 \times \frac{3}{4}$$

Ⓐ <
Ⓑ >
Ⓒ =

10. Order the following products from the least to the greatest

$\frac{3}{7} \times 310,\ 1\frac{1}{2} \times 310,\ \frac{7}{7} \times 310$

Ⓐ $\frac{3}{7} \times 310,\ \frac{7}{7} \times 310,\ 1\frac{1}{2} \times 310$

Ⓑ $1\frac{1}{2} \times 310,\ \frac{7}{7} \times 310,\ \frac{3}{7} \times 310$

Ⓒ $\frac{3}{7} \times 310,\ 1\frac{1}{2} \times 310,\ \frac{7}{7} \times 310$

Ⓓ $1\frac{1}{2} \times 310,\ \frac{7}{7} \times 310,\ \frac{3}{7} \times 310$

Chapter 2

Lesson 3: Representation of Integers

1. Ricky purchased shoes for $159.95 and then exchanged them at a buy 1, get 1 half off sale. The shoes that he purchased on his return trip were $74.99 and $68.55. How much did he receive back from the store after his second transaction?

   Ⓐ $37.50
   Ⓑ $68.55
   Ⓒ $34.28
   Ⓓ $50.68

2. Simplify the following expression:

   $3.24 - 1.914 - 6.025 + 9.86 - 2.2 + 5\dfrac{1}{2} =$

   Ⓐ -8.461
   Ⓑ 8.461
   Ⓒ -11.259
   Ⓓ 11.259

3. John had $76.00. He gave Jim $42.45 and gave Todd $21.34. John will receive $14.50 later in the evening. How much money will John have later that night?

   Ⓐ $25.71
   Ⓑ $26.67
   Ⓒ $26.71
   Ⓓ $24.71

4. Jeri has had a savings account since she entered first grade. Each month of the first year she saved $1.00. Each month of the second year she saved $2.00 etc until she completed ten years in which she saved $10.00 each month. How much does she have saved at the end of ten years?

   Ⓐ $660
   Ⓑ $648
   Ⓒ $636
   Ⓓ $624

5. Which expressions equal - $\frac{3}{4}$? Select all the correct answers.

   Ⓐ $\frac{1}{8}$ - $\frac{7}{8}$

   Ⓑ $\frac{7}{8}$ - $\frac{1}{8}$

   Ⓒ - $\frac{6}{4}$ + $\frac{3}{4}$

   Ⓓ $\frac{1}{4}$ + $\frac{1}{8}$

6. Read the number sentences below and mark the correct property associated with each one.

   $\frac{2}{5}$ + 0 = $\frac{2}{5}$

   Ⓐ Associative Property of Addition
   Ⓑ Inverse Property of Addition
   Ⓒ Identity Property of Addition

7. Brent is walking to the skate park. The park is 3/4 mile from his home. He walked 1/7 mile and realized that he forgot his knee pads. If he must return home for the pads and then walk to the park, how far does he still need to walk?

   Ⓐ $\frac{7}{8}$ mile

   Ⓑ 1 $\frac{7}{8}$ mile

   Ⓒ $\frac{6}{7}$ mile

   Ⓓ $\frac{27}{28}$ mile

8. **Which is NOT true for rational numbers?**

    Ⓐ They will sometimes be written as a fraction with a denominator of 0.
    Ⓑ They can always be removed from the radical symbol.
    Ⓒ They may be positive or negative.
    Ⓓ If not a whole number they may be written as fractions or as decimals.

9. **Kelly started with $660.00 in her savings but every time she did not complete her homework assignments, she lost $5.00. She lost nothing during her first 6 years but in her seventh year she failed to complete 4 assignments. During her eighth year, she completed every assignment. During her ninth year, she failed to complete 6 assignments and during her tenth year, she failed to complete three assignments. How much did she have in savings at the end of ten years?**

    Ⓐ $585
    Ⓑ $590
    Ⓒ $595
    Ⓓ $605

10. **Simplify the following expression:**
    9/10 + (3/8 - 1/3) - (1 1/2 -3/4) =

    Ⓐ $\dfrac{1}{10}$

    Ⓑ $\dfrac{3}{20}$

    Ⓒ $\dfrac{1}{8}$

    Ⓓ $\dfrac{23}{120}$

Chapter 2

Lesson 4: Division of Whole Numbers

1. A team of 12 players got an award of $1,800 for winning a championship football game. If the captain of the team is allowed to keep $315, how much money would each of the other players get? (Assume they split it equally.)

   Ⓐ $135
   Ⓑ $125
   Ⓒ $150
   Ⓓ $123.75

2. Peter gets a salary of $125 per week. He wants to buy a new television that costs $3,960. If he saves $55 per week, which of the following expressions could he use to figure out how many weeks it will take him to save up enough money to buy the new TV?

   Ⓐ $3,960 ÷ ($125 − $55)
   Ⓑ $3,960 − ($125)($55)
   Ⓒ ($3,960 ÷ $125) ÷ $55
   Ⓓ $3,960 ÷ $55

3. An expert typist typed 9,000 words in two hours. How many words per minute did she type?

   Ⓐ 4,500 words per minute
   Ⓑ 150 words per minute
   Ⓒ 75 words per minute
   Ⓓ 38 words per minute

4. Bethany cut off 18 inches of her hair for "Locks of Love". (Locks of Love is a non profit organization that provides wigs to people who have lost their hair due to chemotherapy.) It took her 3 years to grow it back. How much did her hair grow each month?

   Ⓐ 1 inch
   Ⓑ 2 inches
   Ⓒ 0.25 inches
   Ⓓ 0.5 inches

LumosLearning.com

5. On "Jeopardy," during the month of September, the champions won a total of $694,562. Assuming that there were 22 "Jeopardy" shows in September, what was the average amount won each day by the champions?

   Ⓐ $12,435
   Ⓑ $21,891
   Ⓒ $35,176
   Ⓓ $31,571

6. A marching band wants to raise $20,000 at its annual fundraiser. If they sell tickets for $20 a piece, how many tickets will they have to sell?

   Ⓐ 500
   Ⓑ 10,000
   Ⓒ 100
   Ⓓ 1,000

7. A classroom needs 3,200 paper clips for a project. If there are 200 paper clips in a package, how many packages will they need in all?

8. A homebuilder is putting new shelves in each closet he is building. He has 2,592 shelves in his inventory. If each closet needs 108 shelves, how many closets can he build?

9. A toy maker needs to make $17,235 per month to meet his costs. Each toy sells for $45. How many toys does he need to sell in order to break even (cover his costs)?

10. A stamp collector collected 4,224 stamps last year. He collected the same amount each month. How many stamps did he collect each month?

    Ⓐ 422

    Ⓑ 352

    Ⓒ 362

    Ⓓ 252

Chapter 2

Lesson 5: Multiply and divide positive rational numbers

1. Which of the following is equal to $1 \div \frac{3}{4}$? Choose the correct answer choice.

   Ⓐ $\frac{4}{3}$

   Ⓑ $\frac{2}{4}$

   Ⓒ $\frac{1}{3}$

2. Fill in the blank.

   $\frac{1}{2} \div 4 = $ _____?

3. Which of the following is equal to $\frac{7}{2} \div \frac{2}{6}$? Choose the correct answer choice.

   Ⓐ $\frac{9}{2}$

   Ⓑ $\frac{5}{4}$

   Ⓒ $\frac{42}{4}$

4. Three friends went out to lunch together. Ben got a meal that cost $7.25, Frank got a meal that cost $8.16, and Herman got a meal that cost $5.44. If they split the check evenly, how much did they each pay for lunch? (Assume no tax)

   Ⓐ $6.95

   Ⓑ $7.75

   Ⓒ $7.15

   Ⓓ $6.55

5. **Which of these is the standard form of twenty and sixty-three thousandths?**

6. **Mr. Zito bought a bicycle for $160. He spent $12.50 on repair charges. If he sold the same bicycle for $215, what would his profit be on the investment?**

  Ⓐ $ 147.50
  Ⓑ $ 42.50
  Ⓒ $ 67.50
  Ⓓ $ 55.00

7. **A certain book is sold in a paperback version for $4.75 or in a hardcover version for $11.50. If a copy of the book is being purchased for each of the twenty students in Mrs. Jackson's class, how much money altogether would be saved by buying the paperback version, as opposed to the hardcover version?**

  Ⓐ $ 155.00
  Ⓑ $ 135.00
  Ⓒ $ 115.00
  Ⓓ $ 145.00

8. **Which of these sets contains all equivalent numbers?**

  Ⓐ $\left\{ 0.75, \dfrac{3}{4}, 75\%, \dfrac{8}{12} \right\}$

  Ⓑ $\left\{ 0.100, \dfrac{5}{50}, 15\%, 0.010 \right\}$

  Ⓒ $\left\{ \dfrac{3}{8}, 35\%, 0.35, \dfrac{35}{100} \right\}$

  Ⓓ $\left\{ \dfrac{9}{25}, 36\%, 0.360, \dfrac{18}{50} \right\}$

9. Brian is mowing his lawn. He and his family have 7.84 acres. Brian mows 1.29 acres on Monday, 0.85 acres on Tuesday, and 3.63 acres on Thursday. How many acres does Brian have left to mow?

10. Hector is planting his garden. He makes it 5.8 feet wide and 17.2 feet long. What is the area of Hector's garden?

   Ⓐ 9.976 square feet
   Ⓑ 99.76 square feet
   Ⓒ 99.76 feet
   Ⓓ 997.6 square feet

Chapter 2

Lesson 6: Comparison of Rules

1. There are four boxes of pears. Each box has 24 pears. How many pears are there total?

2. Trevor has a collection of 450 baseball cards. He wants to place them into an album. He can fit 15 baseball cards on each page. How can Trevor figure out how many pages he will need to fit into an album all of his cards?

   Ⓐ By adding 450 and 15
   Ⓑ By subtracting 15 from 450
   Ⓒ By multiplying 450 by 15
   Ⓓ By dividing 450 by 15

3. Bow Wow Pet Shop has 12 dogs. Each dog had 4 puppies. How many puppies does the shop have in all?

4. Markers are sold in packs of 18 and 24. Yolanda bought five of the smaller packs and ten of the larger packs. How many markers did she buy altogether?

   Ⓐ 42 markers
   Ⓑ 432 markers
   Ⓒ 320 markers
   Ⓓ 330 markers

5. Each box of cookies contains 48 cookies. About how many cookies would be in 18 boxes?

6. At RTA Elementary School, there are 16 more female teachers than male teachers. If there are 60 female teachers, how can you find the number of male teachers in the school?

   Ⓐ Subtract 16 from 60
   Ⓑ Multiply 16 by 60
   Ⓒ Add 16 to 60
   Ⓓ Divide 60 by 16

7. Consider the following two number sequences:
   x: begin at 2, add 3
   y: begin at 4, add 6
   Which describes the relationship between the number sequences?

   Ⓐ The terms in sequence y are two more than the terms in sequence x.
   Ⓑ The terms in sequence y are six times the terms in sequence x.
   Ⓒ The terms in sequence y are two times the terms in sequence x.
   Ⓓ The terms in sequence y are half as much as the terms in sequence x.

8. Consider the following two number sequences:
   x: begin at 1, multiply by 2
   y: begin at 2, multiply by 2
   Which describes the relationship between the number sequences?

   Ⓐ The terms in sequence y are one more than the terms in sequence x.
   Ⓑ The terms in sequence y are two times the terms in sequence x.
   Ⓒ The terms in sequence y are two more than the terms in sequence x.
   Ⓓ The terms in sequence y are half as much as the terms in sequence x.

9. Consider the following number sequence:
   x: begin at 5, add 6
   Which would result in a relationship in which y is always three more than x?

   Ⓐ y: begin at 8, add 6
   Ⓑ y: begin at 5, add 9
   Ⓒ y: begin at 8, add 9
   Ⓓ y: begin at 2, add 6

10. Consider the following number sequence:
    x: begin at 4, multiply by 2
    Which would result in a relationship in which y is always half as much as x?

    Ⓐ y: begin at 4, multiply by 4
    Ⓑ y: begin at 4, multiply by ½
    Ⓒ y: begin at 2, multiply by 1
    Ⓓ y: begin at 2, multiply by 2

Chapter 2

Lesson 7: Solve real world problems

1. A 12 pack of juice pouches costs $6.00. How much does one juice pouch cost?

2. Eli can ride his scooter 128 miles on one tank of gas. If the scooter has a 4-gallon gas tank, how far can Eli ride on one gallon of gas?

   Ⓐ 64 miles per gallon
   Ⓑ 32 miles per gallon
   Ⓒ 512 miles per gallon
   Ⓓ 20 miles per gallon

3. Clifton ran 6 miles in 39 minutes. At this rate, how much time Clifton takes to run one mile?

   Ⓐ 13 minutes
   Ⓑ 12 minutes
   Ⓒ 7.2 minutes
   Ⓓ 6 minutes and 30 seconds

4. Brad has swimming practice 3 days a week. This week Brad swam a total of 114 laps. At this rate how many laps did Brad swim each day?

5. Karen bought a total of seven items at five different stores. She began with $65.00 and had $15.00 remaining. Which of the following equation can be used to determine the average cost per item?

   Ⓐ $7x \times 5 = \$50.00$
   Ⓑ $7x = \$75.00$
   Ⓒ $7x + \$15.00 = \$65.00$
   Ⓓ $5x = \$65.00 - \$15.00$

6. Geoff goes to the archery range five days a week. He must pay $1.00 for every ten arrows that he shoots. If he spent $15.00 this week on arrows what is the average number of arrows Geoff shot per day?

7. Julia made 7 batches of cookies and ate 3 cookies. There were 74 cookies left. Which expression can be used to determine the average number of cookies per batch?

    Ⓐ $74 \div 7$
    Ⓑ $(74+7) \div 3$
    Ⓒ $\dfrac{74+3}{7}$
    Ⓓ $\dfrac{74}{3} \times 7$

8. Lars delivered 124 papers in 3 hours. How long did it take Lars to deliver one paper?

    Ⓐ 1 minute
    Ⓑ 1 minute and 27 seconds
    Ⓒ 1 minute and 45 seconds
    Ⓓ 2 minutes and 3 seconds

9. Mr. and Mrs. Fink met their son Conrad at the beach. Mr. and Mrs. Fink drove 462 miles on 21 gallons of fuel. Conrad drove 456 miles on 12 gallons of fuel. How many more miles per gallon does Conrad's car get than Mr. and Mrs. Fink's car?

    Ⓐ 6 mpg
    Ⓑ 22 mpg
    Ⓒ 16 mpg
    Ⓓ 38 mpg

10. Myka bought a box of 30 greeting cards for $4.00. Chuck bought a box of 100 greeting cards for $12.00. Who got the better deal?

    Ⓐ Myka got the better deal at about 13 cents per card.
    Ⓑ Myka got the better deal at about 7.5 cents per card.
    Ⓒ Chuck got the better deal at about 8 cents per card.
    Ⓓ Chuck got the better deal at 12 cents per card.

Chapter 2

Lesson 8: Solving Real World Ratio Problems

1. **How many kilograms are there in 375 grams?**

2. **How many inches are there in 2 yards?**

    Ⓐ 24 in
    Ⓑ 36 in
    Ⓒ 48 in
    Ⓓ 72 in

3. **What is 50% of 120?**

4. **Michael Jordan is six feet 6 inches tall. How much is that in inches?**

    Ⓐ 66 inches
    Ⓑ 76 inches
    Ⓒ 86 inches
    Ⓓ 78 inches

5. **What is 7.5% in decimal notation?**

6. **A $60 shirt is on sale for 30% off. How much is the shirt's sale price?**

   Ⓐ $30
   Ⓑ $40
   Ⓒ $18
   Ⓓ $42

7. **On Monday, 6 out of every 10 people who entered a store purchased something. If 1,000 people entered the store on Monday, how many people purchased something?**

   Ⓐ 6 people
   Ⓑ 60 people
   Ⓒ 600 people
   Ⓓ 610 people

8. **If a pair of pants that normally sells for $51.00 is now on sale for $34.00, by what percentage was the price reduced?**

   Ⓐ 30%
   Ⓑ 60%
   Ⓒ 33.33%
   Ⓓ 66.67%

9. **If Comic Book World is taking 28% off the comic books that normally sell for $4.00, how much money is Kevin saving if he buys 12 comic books during the sale?**

   Ⓐ $28
   Ⓑ $12
   Ⓒ $13.44
   Ⓓ $14.58

10. **Eric spends 45 minutes getting to work and 45 minutes returning home. What percent of the day does Eric spend commuting?**

    Ⓐ 6.25%
    Ⓑ 7.8%
    Ⓒ 5.95%
    Ⓓ 15%

Chapter 2

Lesson 9: Quantitative Relationships

1. Logan loves candy! He goes to the store and sees that the bulk candy is $0.79 a pound. Logan wants to buy p pounds of candy and needs to know how much money (m) he needs. Which equation would be used to figure out how much money Logan needs?

    Ⓐ $m = 0.79 \div p$
    Ⓑ $m = 0.79(p)$
    Ⓒ $0.79 = m(p)$
    Ⓓ $m = 0.79 + p$

2. Logan loves candy! He goes to the store and sees that the bulk candy is $0.84 a pound. Logan wants to buy 3 pounds of candy. Using the equation $m = 0.84(p)$, figure out how much money (m) Logan needs.

    Ⓐ $1.68
    Ⓑ $2.52
    Ⓒ $2.25
    Ⓓ $2.54

3. Norman is going on a road trip. He has to purchase gas so that he can make it to his first destination. Gas is $3.55 a gallon. Norman gets g gallons. Which equation would Norman use to figure out how much money (t) it cost to get the gas?

    Ⓐ $t = g(3.55)$
    Ⓑ $t = g \div 3.55$
    Ⓒ $t = 3.55 \div g$
    Ⓓ $t = g + 3.55$

4. Norman is going on a road trip. He has to purchase gas so that he can make it to his first destination. Gas is $3.58 a gallon. Norman needs to get 13 gallons. Using the expression $t = g(3.58)$, figure out how much Norman will spend on gas.

    Ⓐ $46.15
    Ⓑ $39.54
    Ⓒ $46.45
    Ⓓ $46.54

5. Penny planned a picnic for her whole family. It has been very hot outside, so she needs a lot of lemonade to make sure no one is thirsty. There are 60 ounces in each bottle. Penny purchased b bottles of lemonade. She wants to figure out the total number of ounces (o) of lemonade she has. Which equation should she use?

Ⓐ b = 60(o)
Ⓑ 60 = o × b
Ⓒ 60(b) = o
Ⓓ 60 = b ÷ o

6. Ethan is playing basketball in a tournament. Each game lasts 24 minutes. Ethan has 5 games to play. Which general equation could he use to help him figure out the total number of minutes that he played? Let t = the total time, g = the number of games, and m = the time per game.

Ⓐ t = g + m
Ⓑ t = g(m)
Ⓒ t = g − m
Ⓓ t = g ÷ m

7. The Spencers built a new house. They want to plant trees around their house. They want to plant 8 trees in the front yard and 17 in the backyard. The trees that the Spencer's want to plant cost $46 each. Could they use the equation t = c(n) where t is the total cost, c is the cost per tree, and n is the number of trees purchased, to figure out the cost to purchase trees for both the front and the back yards?

Ⓐ No, because the variables represent only two specific numbers that will never change.
Ⓑ Yes, because the variables represent only two specific numbers that will never change.
Ⓒ No, because the variables can be filled in with any number.
Ⓓ Yes, because the variables can be filled in with any number.

8. Liz is a florist. She is putting together b bouquets for a party. Each bouquet is going to have f sunflowers in it. The sunflowers cost $3 each. Which equation can Liz use to figure out the total cost (c) of the sunflowers in the bouquets? Explain your answer.

9. Liz is a florist. She is putting together 5 bouquets for a party. Each bouquet is going to have 6 sunflowers in it. The sunflowers cost $3 each. Using the equation $c = 3(bf)$, figure out how much Liz will charge for the bouquets.

10. Hen B lays 4 times as many eggs as Hen A. (Let a = Number of eggs Hen A lays, b = Number of eggs Hen B lays)

Hen A	Hen B
2	8
4	16
7	28
11	44

Which equation represents this scenario? Explain your answer.

Chapter 2

Lesson 10: Modeling with Expressions

1. Roula had 117 gumballs. Amy had x less than $\frac{1}{2}$ the amount that Roula had. Which expression shows how many gumballs Amy had?

    Ⓐ $117 - \frac{x}{2}$

    Ⓑ $(\frac{1}{2})(117) - x.$

    Ⓒ $117 - 2x$

    Ⓓ $2x + 117$

2. Benny earned $20.00 for weeding the garden. He also earned c dollars for mowing the lawn. Then he spent x dollars at the candy store. Which expression best represents this situation?

    Ⓐ $\$20 - c - x$

    Ⓑ $\$20 + c - x$

    Ⓒ $\$20 + c + x$

    Ⓓ $\$20 + \frac{x}{c}$

3. Clinton loves to cook. He makes a total of 23 different items. Clinton makes 6 different desserts, 12 appetizers, and x main courses. Which equation represents the total amount of food that Clinton cooked?

    Ⓐ $6 - 12 + x = 23$

    Ⓑ $6 + 12 + x = 23$

    Ⓒ $18 - x = 23$

    Ⓓ $6 + 12 - x = 23$

4. Simon has read 694 pages over the summer by reading 3 different books. He read 129 pages in the first book and he read 284 pages in the second book. Which equation shows how to figure out how many pages he read in the third book?

    Ⓐ $694 = 129 + 284 - y$

    Ⓑ $694 = 413 - y$

    Ⓒ $694 = 129 - 284 + y$

    Ⓓ $694 = 129 + 284 + y$

5. Jimmy had $45.00. He spent all of the money on a hat and a pair of jeans. He spent $19.00 on the pair of jeans and x dollars on the hat. Which of the following equations is true?

   Ⓐ $45.00 + x = $19.00
   Ⓑ $45.00 − x = $19.00
   Ⓒ x − $19.00 = $45.00
   Ⓓ $19.00 + 45.00 = x

6. Which of the following equations describes this function?

X	Y
13	104
17	136
20	160
9	72

   Ⓐ y = 18x
   Ⓑ y = x + 4
   Ⓒ y = x + 32
   Ⓓ y = 8x

7. What is the value of x?

   − 7x = 56

8. Does this table show a linear relationship between x and y?

X	Y
13	169
15	225
12	144
20	400
16	256
7	49
8	64

- Ⓐ yes
- Ⓑ no
- Ⓒ yes, but only when x is positive
- Ⓓ yes, but only when y is a perfect square

9. Find the value of z: $\dfrac{z}{5} = 20$

10. Find the value of y: $\dfrac{y}{3} = 12$

Chapter 2

Lesson 11: Representing Inequalities

1. A second grade class raised caterpillars. They had 12 caterpillars. Less than half of the caterpillars turned into butterflies. Which inequality shows how many caterpillars turned into butterflies?

    Ⓐ x < 6
    Ⓑ x > 6
    Ⓒ x ≤ 6
    Ⓓ x ≥ 6

2. Elliot has at least 5 favorite foods. How many favorite foods could Elliot have?

    Ⓐ 4
    Ⓑ 2
    Ⓒ none
    Ⓓ an infinite number

3. Julie has a box full of crayons. Her box of crayons has 549 crayons and at least 8 of them are red. Which inequality represents how many crayons could be red?

    Ⓐ x ≥ 549
    Ⓑ 8 ≥ x ≥ 549
    Ⓒ 8 ≥ x
    Ⓓ 8 ≤ x ≤ 549

4. Five times a number is greater than that number minus 17 is represented as _____.

    Ⓐ 5x > x − 17
    Ⓑ x + 5 > x − 17
    Ⓒ 5x < x − 17
    Ⓓ 5x > x + 17

5. "A number divided by five minus five is less than negative four" is represented as_____ .

    Ⓐ 5x − 5 < −4
    Ⓑ x/5 − 5 < −4
    Ⓒ x/5 − 5 > −4
    Ⓓ x/5 − 5 < 4

6. "Three times the sum of six times a number and three is less than 27." is represented as
    _____.

    Ⓐ 6x + 3 < 27
    Ⓑ 3(6)x + 3 > 27
    Ⓒ 3(6x + 3) < 27
    Ⓓ 6x + 3(3) < 27

7. How would x > 3 be represented on a number line?

    Ⓐ The number line would show an open circle over three with an arrow pointing to the left.
    Ⓑ The number line would show an open circle over three with an arrow pointing to the right.
    Ⓒ The number line would show a closed circle over three with an arrow pointing to the right.
    Ⓓ The number line would show a closed circle over three with an arrow pointing to the left.

8. Amy and Joey each have jellybeans. The amount Amy has is 3 times the amount that Joey has. There are at least 44 jellybeans between them. Which inequality would help you figure out how many jellybeans Amy and Joey each have?

    Ⓐ x + 3x ≥ 44
    Ⓑ 3x ≥ 44
    Ⓒ 3 + x ≥ 44
    Ⓓ x + 3x ≤ 44

9. Sandra is a lawyer. She is working on x number of cases. She gets 8 more cases to work on. She now has more than 29 cases that she is working on. Which inequality could be used to figure out how many cases Sandra is working on?

    Ⓐ 8x > 29
    Ⓑ x + 8 < 29
    Ⓒ x + 8 > 29
    Ⓓ x − 8 < 29

10. There are 25 beehives on a farm. There are the same number of bees in each hive. The total number of bees on the farm is greater than 800. Which inequality could be used to figure out how many bees are in each hive?

    Ⓐ 25/x > 800
    Ⓑ 25x < 800
    Ⓒ 25x > 800
    Ⓓ 25 + x > 800

Chapter 2

Lesson 12: Formation of Equations

1. Bob, the plumber, charges $\frac{1}{4}$ the cost of materials as his labor fee. If his current job has a material cost of $130, how much will Bob charge his client (including his labor fee)?

   (A) $162.50
   (B) $32.50
   (C) $130.25
   (D) None of the above

2. A box has a length of 6x inches. The width equals one third the length, and the height equals half the length. If the volume equals 972 cubic inches, what does x equal?

3. Taylor is trimming the shrubbery along three sides of his backyard. The backyard is rectangular in shape. The length of the backyard is twice its width and the total perimeter is 180 feet. The shrubbery that Taylor needs to trim is along three sides of the rectangular backyard (along the two lengths and one width). Find the total length of the shrubbery that he needs to trim.

   (A) 180 ft
   (B) 120 ft
   (C) 90 ft
   (D) 150 ft

4. Jim is 4 years older than his brother Bob. In two years, Jim will be twice Bob's age. How old are they now?

   (A) Bob is 6 and Jim is 10.
   (B) Bob is 4 and Jim is 8.
   (C) Bob is 0 and Jim is 4.
   (D) Bob is 2 and Jim is 6.

5. In a certain classroom, the ratio of boys to girls is 2 to 1. If there are 39 students in the classroom, how many are boys?

6. John put three gallons of gasoline into his truck. The gasoline level was at 10% before he added the gasoline. If the truck has a 12 gallon tank, how much more gasoline can fit in the tank?

    Ⓐ 7.8 gallons
    Ⓑ 6.7 gallons
    Ⓒ 8.9 gallons
    Ⓓ 10.8 gallons

7. Melanie has $35.00 in her savings account and does cleaning in a neighbor's house for $15.00 per week. Sue has no money saved, but is mowing lawns at $20.00 each. If Sue mows 1 lawn per week, how long will it take her to catch up with Melanie?

    Ⓐ 5 weeks
    Ⓑ 6 weeks
    Ⓒ 7 weeks
    Ⓓ 8 weeks

8. Sissy is baking cookies for her class party. She plans to bake 128 cookies. Her recipe makes 6 dozen cookies. If her recipe calls for 3 1/2 c flour, how much flour will she need to make 128 cookies (round to the nearest half cup)?

    Ⓐ $5\frac{1}{2}$ c
    Ⓑ 4 c
    Ⓒ $4\frac{1}{2}$ c
    Ⓓ 6 c

9. Jenn went to the farmer's market with $40.00. She bought a 10 lb bag of potatoes for $6.00, a pie for $8.00, 4 qt fresh blueberries for $4.00 per qt, and 5 lb of apples at $1.49 per lb. What percent of the $40.00 did she still have when she left?

    Ⓐ 93.625%
    Ⓑ 6.375%
    Ⓒ 25%
    Ⓓ .0595%

10. Nelly spent $\frac{7}{8}$ of his savings on furniture and the rest on a lawnmower. If the lawnmower cost him $250, how much did he spend on furniture?

    Ⓐ $2000
    Ⓑ $1750
    Ⓒ $1500
    Ⓓ $1000

Chapter 2

Lesson 13: Equations and Inequalities

1. How many positive whole number solutions (values for x) does this inequality have?
   x ≤ 20

2. Which of the following correctly shows the number sentence that the following words describe? 17 is less than or equal to the product of 6 and q.

   Ⓐ 17 ≤ 6q
   Ⓑ 17 ≤ 6 – q
   Ⓒ 17 < 6q
   Ⓓ 17 ≥ 6q

3. Which of the following correctly shows the number sentence that the following words describe? The quotient of d and 5 is 15.

   Ⓐ $\dfrac{5}{d} = 15$

   Ⓑ 5d = 15

   Ⓒ $\dfrac{d}{5} = 15$

   Ⓓ d – 5 = 15

4. Which of the following correctly shows the number sentence that the following words describe? Three times the quantity u – 4 is less than 17

   Ⓐ 3(u – 4) > 17
   Ⓑ 3(u – 4) < 17
   Ⓒ 3(u – 4) ≤ 17
   Ⓓ 3(u – 4) ≥ 17

5. Which of the following correctly shows the number sentence that the following words describe? The difference between z and the quantity 7 minus r is 54.

Ⓐ $z - 7 - r = 54$
Ⓑ $z + 7 - r = 54$
Ⓒ $z + (7 - r) = 54$
Ⓓ $z - (7 - r) = 54$

6. Which of the following correctly shows the number sentence that the following words describe? The square of the sum of 6 and b is greater than 10.

Ⓐ $(6 + b)^2 > 10$
Ⓑ $6^2 + b^2 > 10$
Ⓒ $(6 + b)^2 = 10$
Ⓓ $(6 + b)^2 < 10$

7. Which of the following correctly shows the number sentence that the following words describe? 16 less than the product of 5 and h is 21.

Ⓐ $16 - 5h = 21$
Ⓑ $5h - 16 = 21$
Ⓒ $16 - (5 + h) = 21$
Ⓓ $16 < 5h + 21$

8. Which of the following correctly shows the number sentence that the following words describe? 8 times the quantity 2x – 7 is greater than 5 times the quantity 3x + 9.

Ⓐ $8(2x) - 7 > 5(3x) + 9$
Ⓑ $8(2x - 7) \geq 5(3x + 9)$
Ⓒ $8(2x - 7) > 5(3x + 9)$
Ⓓ $8(2x - 7) < 5(3x + 9)$

9. A batting cage offers 8 pitches for a quarter. Raul has $1.50. Which expression could be used to calculate how many pitches Raul could get for his money?

Ⓐ $\$1.50 \times 8$
Ⓑ $\$1.50 \div 8$
Ⓒ $(\$1.50 \div \$0.25) \times 8$
Ⓓ $(\$1.50 \div \$0.25)$

10. For which of the following values of x is this inequality true?
    500 − 3x > 80

    (A) x = 100
    (B) x = 150
    (C) x = 210
    (D) x = 120

End of Computations and Algebraic Relationships

Answer Key and Detailed Explanations

Chapter 2: Computations and Algebraic Relationships

Lesson 1: Division of Fractions

Question No.	Answer	Detailed Explanation
1	80	The original problem is: $$\frac{20}{1} \div \frac{1}{4} =$$ To divide fractions, you must Keep (the first fraction), Change (the division to multiplication), and Flip (the second fraction, or, take the reciprocal). $$\frac{20}{1} \times \frac{4}{1} = \frac{80}{1} = 80$$
2	D	The original problem is: $$1\frac{1}{2} \div \frac{3}{4} =$$ First, find the improper fraction of the first mixed number (numerator = bottom times the side plus the top) = [(2*1)+1], Fraction = $\frac{3}{2}$ To divide fractions, you must keep (the first fraction), Change (the division to multiplication), Flip (the second fraction, or, take the reciprocal). $$\frac{3}{2} \times \frac{4}{3} = \frac{12}{6}$$ Simplify by factoring out the GCF of 6. The answer is $\frac{2}{1}$ or 2
3	D	The original problem is: $$3\frac{2}{3} \div 2\frac{1}{6} =$$ First, find the improper fraction of the first mixed number (numerator = bottom times the side plus the top) = [(3*3)+2], Fraction=$\frac{11}{3}$. Then, find the improper fraction of the second mixed number (numerator = bottom times the side plus the top = [(2*6)+1], Fraction = $\frac{13}{6}$ To divide fractions, you must keep (the first fraction), Change (the division to multiplication), Flip (the second fraction, or, take the reciprocal). $$\frac{11}{3} \times \frac{6}{13} = \frac{66}{39}$$ Simplify by factoring out the GCF of 3. The answer is $\frac{22}{13}$ Divide $\frac{22}{13}$ to get a mixed number: The answer is $1\frac{9}{13}$.

Question No.	Answer	Detailed Explanation
4	A	The original problem is: $2\dfrac{3}{4} \div \dfrac{11}{4} =$ First convert the mixed fraction into improper fraction by using Numerator of the improper fraction = denominator of mixed fraction x whole part of the mixed fraction + numerator of the mixed fraction whereas the denominator of the improper fraction is same as that of the mixed fraction. $2\dfrac{3}{4} \div \dfrac{11}{4} = \dfrac{11}{4} \div \dfrac{11}{4} = 1$
5	A	The original problem is: $\dfrac{7}{8} \div \dfrac{3}{4} =$ Division of fractions can be obtained by multiplying the dividend with the reciprocal of the divisor. Thus, $\dfrac{7}{8} \div \dfrac{3}{4} = \dfrac{7}{8} \times \dfrac{4}{3} = \dfrac{28}{24} = \dfrac{7}{6} = 1\dfrac{1}{6}$
6	D	The original problem is: $6\dfrac{3}{4} \div 1\dfrac{1}{8} =$ First convert the mixed fractions into improper fraction by using Numerator of the improper fraction = denominator of mixed fraction x whole part of the mixed fraction + numerator of the mixed fraction whereas the denominator of the improper fraction is same as that of the mixed fraction. So, $6\dfrac{3}{4} \div 1\dfrac{1}{8} = \dfrac{27}{4} \div \dfrac{8}{9}$ Division of fractions can be obtained by multiplying the dividend with the reciprocal of the divisor. Thus, $\dfrac{27}{4} \div \dfrac{9}{8} = \dfrac{27}{4} \times \dfrac{8}{9}$ Cross factor out the GCF of 4 from 4 and 8 Cross factor out the GCF of 9 from 9 and 27 $\dfrac{3}{1} \times \dfrac{2}{1} = 6$

Question No.	Answer	Detailed Explanation
7	35	To divide the fractions, you must Keep (the first fraction), Change (the division to multiplication), and Flip (the second fraction, or, take the reciprocal). The second fraction then reads $\frac{5}{1}$. Because $\frac{5}{1}$ is the same as 5, the problem simplifies to 7 X 5 = 35.
8	11	Since $\frac{6}{6}$ is equal to 1, the problem simplifies to 11 divided by 1. The answer is 11.
9	C	When any fraction is multiplied by its reciprocal, the cross numerators and denominators will always factor to 1.
10	B	$\frac{14}{21} \div \frac{28}{7}$ Becomes $\frac{14}{21} \times \frac{7}{28}$ After Keep−Change−Flip. Then, cross factor out a GCF of 7 from the 14 and 21, and a GCF of 7 from the 7 and 28. The simplified problem becomes: $\frac{2}{3} \times \frac{1}{4}$

Lesson 2: Numbers multiplied by fractions

Question No.	Answer	Detailed Explanation
1	A	Multiplying a number by a fraction less than 1 will result in a product that is less than the original number.
2	D	Multiplying a number by a fraction greater than 1 will result in a product that is greater than the original number.
3	B	Multiplying a number by a fraction greater than 1 will result in a product that is greater than the original number. Since the second factor is only $\frac{1}{7}$ more than one, the product will be just slightly greater than 18,612. The only other option that is greater than 18,612 (option C: 36,000) is more than twice the original number.
4	B	Multiplying a number by a fraction greater than 1 will result in a product that is greater than the original number. Since the product is only slightly greater than the original number, the other factor will be just slightly greater than 1. Therefore, $\frac{4}{3}$ (which is equal to $1\frac{1}{3}$) is the only option possible.
5	C	Multiplying a number by a fraction less than 1 will result in a product that is less than the original number. Since the fraction is only slightly less than 1, the other factor will be just slightly greater than 17,365. Therefore, 20,838 is the only option possible, as 50,838 is more than double the product.
6	B & C	When multiplying a whole number by a fraction, if the fraction is less than one, the product will be less than the whole number. If the fraction is greater than one, the product will be greater than the whole number. The fractions that are greater than one are $\frac{10}{9}$ and $\frac{3}{2}$. Therefore 6 times either of these fractions will result in a product greater than 6. The correct answer choices are B and C.

Question No.	Answer	Detailed Explanation
7		When multiplying a whole number by a fraction, if the fraction is less than one, the product will be less than < the whole number. if the fraction is greater than one, the product will be greater than the whole number. Since $\frac{2}{3}$ is less than 1, $5 \times \frac{2}{3} < 5$ Since $\frac{4}{3}$ is greater than 1, $\frac{4}{3} \times 8 > 8$ Since $\frac{4}{7}$ is less than 1, $12 \times \frac{4}{7} < 12$ Since $\frac{24}{24}$ is equal to 1, $4 \times \frac{24}{24} = 4$
8	C	When multiplying a whole number by a fraction, if the fraction is less than one, the product will be less than the whole number. If the fraction is greater than one, the product will be greater than the whole number. Since $\frac{9}{15}$ is less than 1, $\frac{9}{15} \times 16 < 16$. Therefore $\frac{9}{15} \times 16 < 16$ is a true statement.
9	B	$44 \times \frac{3}{4} = 11 \times 3 = 33$ $44 > 33$ The choice B is the correct answer.
10	A	$\frac{3}{7} \times 310$ will be less than 310 $\frac{7}{7} \times 310$ will be 310 since $\frac{7}{7}$ is 1 $1\frac{1}{2} \times 310$ will be greater than 310 The choice A is the correct answer.

Lesson 3: Representation of Integers

Question No.	Answer	Detailed Explanations
1	D	On his second trip to the store he paid $74.99 plus half of $68.55. $74.99 + $34.28 = $109.27 $159.95 - 109.27 = $50.68 $50.68 is the correct answer.
2	B	First, we will change 5 1/2 to 5.5. Then we have 3.24 - 1.914 - 6.025 +9.86 -2.2 + 5.5 = 8.461 8.461 is the correct answer.
3	C	To solve this problem, list all the monetary values, along with the proper operation, before evaluating it. For this problem, words like "give" mean to subtract, while "receives" means to add. (1) 76.00 - 42.45 - 21.34 + 14.50 = (2) 33.55 - 21.34 + 14.50 = (3) 12.21 + 14.50 = (4) 26.71 Therefore, John will have $26.71 later that night.
4	A	Year 1 - $12.00, Year 2 - $24.00. Year 3 - $36.00. Year 4 - $48.00. Year 5 - $60.00. Year 6 - $72.00. Year 7 - $84.00. Year 8 - $96.00. Year 9 - $108.00. Year 10 - $120.00 Adding the totals for each year, we get $660.00. $660.00 is the correct answer.
5	A and C	$-\frac{6}{4} + \frac{3}{4}$ add the numerators and you get -3. So the fraction is $-\frac{3}{4}$ $\frac{1}{8} - \frac{7}{8} = 1 - 7 = -6$ and $\frac{-6}{8}$ simplifies to $\frac{-3}{4}$

Question No.	Answer	Detailed Explanations
6	C	The associative property of addition means that you can move grouping symbols and it does not change the value of the expression. The inverse property of addition means that you can add a number and its inverse together and you will get 0. The identity property of addition states that if you add 0 to a number it will not change the value.
7	D	Brent needs to walk 1/7 mile back home and then 3/4 mile to the park. $1/7 + 3/4 = 4/28 + 21/28 = 25/28$ of a mile total 25/28 is the correct answer.
8	A	By definition, rational numbers are numbers that can be written as the quotient of two numbers where the denominator is not zero. "They will sometimes be written as a fraction with a denominator of 0" is the correct answer.
9	C	Kelly failed to complete a total of 13 assignments. She lost $5.00 for each of 13 assignments or a total of $65.00. This left her with $660 - $65 = $595.00. $595 is the correct answer.
10	D	$9/10 + (3/8 - 1/3) - (1\ 1/2 - 3/4) =$ Let's first remove parentheses. $9/10 + 3/8 - 1/3 - 1\ 1/2 + 3/4 =$ LCD is 120; so expression becomes $108/120 + 45/120 - 40/120 - 180/120 + 90/120 = 23/120$ 23/120 is the correct answer.

Lesson 4: Division of Whole Numbers

Question No.	Answer	Detailed Explanations
1	A	First, find the difference of $1,800 − $315 = $1,485 Then, divide $1,485/11 = $135
2	D	To find the answer, divide $3,960 ÷ 55. (Note: The $125 is unnecessary information.)
3	C	1 hour = 60 minutes, so 2 hours = 120 minutes So, 9,000 ÷ 120 = 75
4	D	1 year = 12 months, so 3 years = 36 months 18 ÷ 36 =0.5 inches per month.
5	D	Use long division. $694,562 ÷ 22 = $31,571
6	D	Let the number of tickets to be sold be n. Therefore, n * 20 = 20000 n = 20000 / 20 n = 1000
7	16	Number of packages(n) = Total number of clips required/Number of clips in one package n = 3200 / 200 n = 16
8	24	Number of closets that can be built(n) = Total number of shelves/Number of shelves in each closet n = 2592 / 108 n = 24
9	383	Use long division. $17,235 ÷ $45 = 383
10	B	Use the standard long division algorithm. 4,224 ÷ 12 = 352

Lesson 5: Multiply and divide positive rational numbers

Question No.	Answer	Detailed Explanations
1	A	$\frac{4}{3}$. Because $1 \div \frac{3}{4} = \frac{1}{1} \times \frac{4}{3} = \frac{4}{3}$
2	$\frac{1}{8}$	$\frac{1}{8}$. Because $\frac{1}{2} \div \frac{4}{1} = \frac{1}{2} \times \frac{1}{4} = \frac{1}{8}$
3	C	$\frac{42}{4}$. Because $\frac{7}{2} \div \frac{2}{6} = \frac{7}{2} \times \frac{6}{2} = \frac{42}{4}$
4	A	$\$7.25 + \$8.16 + \$5.44 = \$20.85$ $\$20.85/3 = \$6.95$
5	20.063	The standard form would be written as 20.063 since the whole number part is 20 and the decimal part is written .063 (Sixty-three thousandths).
6	B	$\$160 + \$12.50 = \$172.50$ (His total investment) $\$215.00 - \$172.50 = \$42.50$
7	B	$\$11.50*20 = \$230$ $\$4.75*20 = \$95$ $\$230 - \$95 = \$135$ $\$135.00$ would be saved by purchasing the paperback book
8	D	The last set is the only set of numbers that are all equivalent. These numbers all have a decimal equivalent of 0.36.
9	2.07	$1.29 + 0.85 + 3.63 = 5.77$ $7.84 - 5.77 = 2.07$ acres left to mow
10	B	Multiply the length by width to find the area. $5.8 * 17.2$ Multiply the numbers and find the product. Then, count the decimal places in the factors. There is one decimal place for each factor or a total of two decimal places. Count two spaces from the right and put the decimal point in your answer. $5.8 * 17.2 = 99.76$

Lesson 6: Comparison of Rules

Question No.	Answer	Detailed Explanations
1	96	Each box has 24 pears and there are 4 boxes, so that is 24 x 4, which equals 96.
2	D	The total collection is 450. Each page will have 15 cards or parts of the whole. When you divide 450 by 15, the answer tells how many pages are needed.
3	48	There are 12 dogs in Bow Wow Pet Shop. Since, each dog has 4 puppies, the total number of puppies will be 12 x 4 which is equals to 48.
4	D	This problem requires 2 steps. There were (5) 18 count packs bought. Multiply 5 x 18 = 90. There were (10) 24 count packs bought. Multiply 10 x 24 = 240. Add the two products together to find out the sum or total amount bought. 240 + 90, which equals 330.
5	1000	The question begins with the word, "about", which means to estimate. Begin by rounding off the number of cookies. 48 rounds off to 50. Multiply that estimate by the number of boxes: 50 x 18 = 900. Of the four estimate choices, 1,000 is the closest estimate. Also note 18 can be rounded to 20.
6	A	This is a subtraction problem. There are 60 female teachers, however, there are 16 more of them than male teachers. Hence, the number of male teachers will be 60 - 16.
7	C	According to the rules, sequence x would begin 2, 5, 8, ..., and sequence y would begin 4, 10, 16, ... Therefore, the terms in sequence y are always two times the terms in sequence x.
8	B	According to the rules, sequence x would begin 1, 2, 4, ..., and sequence y would begin 2, 4, 8, ... Therefore, the terms in sequence y are always two times the terms in sequence x.
9	A	Sequence x : 5, 11, 17, ... According to the rule in option A, sequence y : 8, 14, 20, ... Therefore, the terms in sequence y are always three more than the terms in sequence x. Option (A) is the Correct Answer. Note that, once we get the correct option, we need check the other options.

Question No.	Answer	Detailed Explanations
10	D	Sequence x : 4, 8, 16,.... Sequence y in option (A) : 4, 16, 64 ..... comparing sequence x and sequence y, we see that given rule is NOT satisfied. So, option (A) is incorrect. Sequence y in option (B) : 4, 2, 1 .... comparing sequence x and sequence y, we see that given rule is NOT satisfied. So, option (B) is incorrect. Sequence y in option (C) : 2, 2, 2 ... comparing sequence x and sequence y, we see that given rule is NOT satisfied. So, option (C) is incorrect. Sequence y in option (D) : 2, 4, 8 .... comparing sequence x and sequence y, we see that terms in sequence y are always half as much as the terms in sequence x. So, option (D) is correct.

Lesson 7: Solve real world problems

Question No.	Answer	Detailed Explanations
1	$0.50	Find the unit rate for one juice pouch. $$\frac{\$6.00}{12} = \frac{x}{1}$$ 6*1=12*x 6 = 12x Divide both sides by 12 x = $0.50 per pouch
2	B	Find the unit rate for one gallon of gas. $$\frac{128}{4} = \frac{x}{1}$$ 128*1=4*x 128 = 4x Divide both sides by 4 x = 32 miles per gallon
3	D	Find the unit rate for one mile. $$\frac{39}{6} = \frac{x}{1}$$ 39*1=6*x 39 = 6x Divide both sides by 6 x = 6.5 or 6 minutes 30 seconds
4	38 laps	Find the unit rate for one day. $$\frac{114}{3} = \frac{x}{1}$$ 114*1=3*x 114 = 3x Divide both sides by 3 x = 38 laps per day
5	C	The cost of the seven items plus $15.00 should equal $65.00. If the average cost per item is x, then 7x is the cost of all seven items. Therefore 7x + $15.00 = $65.00 can be used to find x.
6	30 arrows	Find the unit rate for one day. Geoff shot 150 arrows ($15*10) $$\frac{150}{5} \text{ days} = \frac{x}{1}$$ 150*1=5*x 150 = 5x Divide both sides by 5 x = 30 arrows per day

Question No.	Answer	Detailed Explanations
7	C	Find the total number of cookies and divide by 7. The total number of cookies is 74 + 3 = 77. The number of batches is 7. So the total number of cookies per batch can be found using the expression (74 + 3)/7.
8	B	Find the unit rate for one paper. Change hours to minutes or 3 hrs = 3*60 mins $$\frac{180}{124} = \frac{x}{1}$$ 180*1=124*x 180 = 124x Divide both sides by 124 x = 1.45 minutes or 1 minutes and 27 seconds
9	C	Find the unit rate for both and compare. Fink's: 462 miles/21 gallons = 22 miles per gallon Conrad's: 456 miles/12 gallons = 38 gallons Difference: 38 − 22 = 16 gallons
10	D	Find the unit rate for both and compare. Myka: $4.00/30 cards = $0.13 per card Chuck: $12.00/100 cards = $0.12 per card Chuck paid 12 cents per card and Myka paid 13 cents per card. So Chuck got the better deal.

Lesson 8: Solving Real World Ratio Problems

Question No.	Answer	Detailed Explanations
1	0.375 kilograms	1000 grams/1 kilogram = 375 grams/x kilograms 1000x = 375 Divide each side by 1000 x = 0.375 kilograms
2	D	36 inches equal 1 yard, so 72 inches must equal 2 yards.
3	60	is/of = %/100 so: $\frac{x}{120} = \frac{50}{100}$ 100*x = 120*50 100x = 6000 Divide both sides by 100 x = 60
4	D	Since every foot = 12 inches, then 6 feet must equal 72 inches (6*12). Add extra 6 inches to 72 inches which is equal to 78 inches.
5	0.075	Divide a percentage by 100 to make an equivalent decimal form 7.5/100 = .075
6	D	is/of = %/100 $\frac{x}{60} = \frac{30}{100}$ x*100 = 60*30 100x = 1800 Divide both sides by 100 x = $18 Subtract $18 from $60. $60−$18 = $42
7	C	$\frac{6}{10} = \frac{x}{1000}$ x*10 = 6*1000 10x = 6000 Divide both sides by 10 x = 600

Question No.	Answer	Detailed Explanations
8	C	is/of = %/100 $\dfrac{34.00}{51.00} = \dfrac{x}{100}$ 34.00*100 = 51*x 3400 = 51x Divide both sides by 51 x = 66.67% This is the amount left to pay. 100% − 66.67% = 33.33% This is the amount the shirt was reduced by.
9	C	is/of = %/100 $\dfrac{x}{\$4.00} = \dfrac{28}{100}$ 4*28 = 100*x 112 = 100x Divide both sides by 100 x = $1.12 Then, multiply $1.12 * 12 = $13.44
10	A	is/of = x/100 use hours as your proportional rate 45 minutes + 45 minutes = 90 minutes or 1.5 hours $\dfrac{1.5}{24} = \dfrac{x}{100}$ 1.5*100 = 24*x 150 = 24x Divide both sides by 24 x = 6.25%

Lesson 9: Quantitative Relationships

Question No.	Answer	Detailed Explanations
1	B	"m" represents the amount of money that Logan needs. "p" represents the number of pounds that Logan buys. The amount of money Logan needs is found by multiplying the cost of the candy by the number of pounds that Logan buys. m = 0.79(p)
2	B	m = \$0.84(3) m = \$2.52
3	A	"t" represents the total amount Norman spent. "g" represents the number of gallons that Norman purchased. To find the total amount that Norman spent, multiply the price of the gas by the total number of gallons that Norman purchased. t = g(3.55)
4	D	t = 13 gallons (\$3.58) t = 13(3.58) t = 46.54 \$46.54
5	C	"b" represents the number of bottles of lemonade "o" represents the total number of ounces of lemonade To find out the total number of ounces of lemonade that Penny purchased, multiply the number of bottles (b) by the number of ounces in each bottle, 60. 60(b) = o
6	B	"t" represents the total number of minutes Ethan played "g" represents the number of games "m" represent the number of minutes in each game To find out the total number of minutes Ethan played, multiply the number of games by the number of minutes in each game. t = g(m)
7	D	The equation t = c(n) can be used with any numbers. The equation has the number of trees and the cost of one tree as variables. Those quantities, no matter what they are, when multiplied together will always equal the total cost.

Question No.	Answer	Detailed Explanations
8	c = 3(bf)	"c" represents the total cost "b" represents the number of bouquets "f" represents the number of sunflowers To find the total cost, multiply the number of bouquets by the number of sunflowers by the price of the sunflowers. c = 3(bf)
9	$90	c = 3(bf) c = 3(6)(5) c = 90 $90
10	b = 4a	The number of eggs that Hen B lays depends on the number of eggs that Hen A lays. Hen B lays 4 times more than Hen A. That is represented as 4a b = 4a

Lesson 10: Modeling with Expressions

Question No.	Answer	Detailed Explanations
1	B	Half of 117 can be expressed as (1/2)(117). x less than that is expressed as − x. (1/2)(117) − x.
2	B	Start with $20.00. Then add what he earned mowing the lawn (+c). Then subtract what he spent at the candy store (−x). The expression is $20 + c − x.
3	B	Clinton made a total of 23 items, so you know the expression has to equal 23. He made 6 desserts and 12 appetizers. You do not know how many main courses he made, so that is represented by x. 6 + 12 + x = 23
4	D	Simon read a total of 694 pages. Add the pages from the first book (129), the second book (284) and the third book (y) together. 694 = 129 + 284 + y
5	B	Subtracting the cost of the hat (x) from the total cost ($45.00) would leave the cost of the jeans ($19.00). $45.00 − x = $19.00.
6	D	Each time a number from x is multiplied by 8, the product is found in y. So, the equation is y = 8x.
7	−8	To find the value of x, you must isolate it. Divide each side by −7. − 7x/−7 = 56/−7. x = −8
8	B	Each value of y is the square of the corresponding x value. This is not a linear relationship.
9	100	$\frac{z}{5} = 20$ To find the value of z, you must isolate it. Multiply each side by 5/1 to cancel out the denominator and isolate the z. z/5 * 5/1 = z 20 * 5/1 = 100 so, z = 100
10	36	$\frac{y}{3} = 12$ To find the value of y, you must isolate it. Multiply by 3 on each side to isolate the y. y/3*(3/1) = 12(3/1) y = 36

Lesson 11: Representing Inequalities

Question No.	Answer	Detailed Explanations
1	A	Half of 12 is 6. Less than 6 caterpillars turned into butterflies. That means that x < 6.
2	D	Elliot has at least 5 different favorite foods. That means that he has more than 5 favorite foods. He could have an infinite number of favorite foods because there is no constraint on the number of favorite foods he could have.
3	D	There can be no more than 549 red crayons because that is the maximum number of crayons in the box. You know there are at least 8 red crayons, which means that x is greater than or equal to 8 and less than or equal to 549. $8 \leq x \leq 549$
4	A	"Five times a number" is represented as 5x. "Is greater than" is represented as >. "That number minus 17" is represented as x − 17. 5x > x − 17
5	B	"A number divided by 5" is represented as x/5. "Minus five" is represented as − 5. "Is less than" is represented as <. "Negative four" is represented as −4. x/5 −5 < −4
6	C	"A number times six plus three" is represented as 6x + 3. Three times that is represented as 3(6x + 3). "Is less than" is represented as <. 3(6x + 3) < 27
7	B	An open circle means that the number the circle is over is not included in the answer. An arrow pointing to the right means "greater than". The number line would show an open circle over three with an arrow pointing to the right.
8	A	The number of jellybeans that Joey has is represented as x. Amy has three times that many so that is represented as 3x. Together they have at least 44. That means that their jellybeans added together are at least 44, so that is represented as x + 3x. At least means that they could have 44 or more than 44 so that is represented as ≥ x + 3x ≥ 44

Question No.	Answer	Detailed Explanations
9	C	The number of cases that Sandra has is represented as x. The 8 more she gets is represented as x + 8. She has more than 29, so that is represented as > 29 $x + 8 > 29$
10	C	The number of bees in each hive is represented as x. There are the same number of bees in all 25 beehives. The total number of bees is represented as 25x. The total number of bees on the farm is greater than 800. Greater than is represented as > 800. $25x > 800$

Lesson 12: Formation of Equations

Question No.	Answer	Detailed Explanations
1	A	In order to find out how much Bill should charge his client, divide 130 by 4, and then add the quotient to 130: (1) 130 ÷ 4 = 32.50 (2) 130 + 32.50 = $162.50
2	3	First, write the expressions based on the language in the problem: length = 6x width = $(\frac{1}{3})(6x)$ height = $(\frac{1}{2})(6x)$ Next, solve for x based on the formula for volume, lwh. (1) $6x \times ((\frac{1}{3})(6x)) \times ((\frac{1}{2})(6x)) = 972$ (2) $6x \times 2x \times 3x = 972$ (3) $12x^2 \times 3x = 972$ (4) $36x^3 = 972$ (divide each side by 36) (5) $x^3 = 27$ (6) $x = 3$
3	D	Let x be the width of the rectangular backyard. Length = 2x. Perimeter of the backyard = x + 2x + x + 2x = 180 ft. 6x = 180 ft. $x = \frac{180}{6}$ = 30 ft. = width of the backyard. Length of the backyard = 2x = 60 ft. Total length of the shrubbery Taylor needs to trim = width+length+length = x + 2x + 2x = 150 ft.
4	D	Now : Bob's age = x, Jim's age = x + 4 In 2 years : Bob's age = x + 2, Jim's age = x + 4 + 2 = x + 6 It is given that, in 2 years, Jim's age is twice Bob's age. Therefore, we have, x + 6 = 2(x + 2) x + 6 = 2x + 4 2 = x = Bob 6 = x + 4 = Jim Bob is 2, and Jim is 6.
5	26	Let x = number of girls, 2x = number of boys, x + 2x = 39, 3x = 39, x = 13, girls 2x = 26 boys
6	A	First, set up the equation based on the language of the problem: (1) Amount of gas = 3 gallons (2) Gas level = 10% (3) Tank capacity = 12 gallons (4) x = Amount of gallons needed to fill tank (5) Equation = 12 - (12(0.10) + 3) = x Next, solve for x (6) 12 - (1.2 + 3) = x (7) 12 - 4.2 = x (8) 7.8 gallons
7	C	Let n = number of weeks of work for Sue to catch up with Melanie 35 + 15n = 20n, 35 = 5n, 7 = n 7 weeks is the correct answer.
8	D	6 dozen = 72 cookies $\frac{128}{72} = 1\frac{56}{72} = 1\frac{7}{9}$ recipes $1\frac{7}{9} \times 3\frac{1}{2} = 6.22$ cups 6 c is the correct answer.

Question No.	Answer	Detailed Explanations
9	B	She spent 4 x $4.00 = $16.00 for blueberries and 5 x $1.49 = $7.45 for apples and $6.00 for potatoes and $8.00 for a pie $37.45 Total $40.00 - $37.45 = $2.55 left $\frac{\$2.55}{\$40.00}=.06375= 6.375\%$ left
10	B	$\frac{8}{8} - \frac{7}{8} = \frac{1}{8}$ on lawnmower $(\frac{1}{8})s = 250$, $s = 8(250)$, $s = \$2000$, (total savings) $\frac{7}{8} (2000) = \frac{14000}{8} = 1750$. $1750 is the correct answer.

Lesson 13: Equations and Inequalities

Question No.	Answer	Detailed Explanations
1	19	x can be any whole number from 1 to 20, inclusive of 20.
2	A	"17 is less than or equal to" means 17 ≤ "the product of 6 and q" means to multiply 6 and q, or 6q 17 ≤ 6q
3	C	"The quotient of d and 5" means to divide d by 5 "is 15" means "equals 15". $\frac{d}{5} = 15$
4	B	"Three times the quantity u − 4" means to multiply (u−4) by 3 → 3(u−4) "is less than 17" means < 17 3(u−4) < 17
5	D	"The difference between z and the quantity 7 minus r" means to find the difference between z and (7−r), so z − (7−r) "is 54" means equals 54 So, z − (7 − r) = 54
6	A	"The square of the sum of 6 and b" means to square all of (6 + b), or $(6 + b)^2$ "is greater than 10" means "> 10" $(6 + b)^2 > 10$
7	B	"16 less than" means to "subtract 16 from some term" "the product of 5 and h" means to multiply 5 and h or "5h" "is 21" means "equals 21" 5h − 16 = 21
8	C	"8 times the quantity 2x – 7" means to multiply 8 and 2x − 7, which needs to be in parentheses (as a quantity), so 8(2x − 7) "is greater than" means ">" 5 times the quantity 3x + 9" means 5 multiplied by 3x + 9, which needs to be in parentheses (as a quantity), so 5(3x+9) 8(2x − 7) > 5(3x + 9)
9	C	To find how many quarters (or the equivalent of how many quarters) Raul has, you could calculate $1.50 divided by $0.25. Then, that amount of quarters would be multiplied by 8, the number of pitches purchased with each quarter. The final expression would read: ($1.50 ÷ $0.25) x 8

Question No.	Answer	Detailed Explanations
10	A and D	Solve to find x: $500 - 3x > 80$ First, subtract 500 from both sides $-3x > -420$ Next, divide both sides by -3. (Don't forget to switch the inequality sign when dividing a negative in an inequality) $x < 140$ So, $x = 120$ and $x = 100$ would work as a solution.

Chapter 3:
Geometry and Measurement

Chapter 3

Lesson 1: Measurement Conversion

1. Owen is 69 inches tall. How tall is Owen in feet?

2. What is 7 gallons 3 quarts expressed as quarts?

3. How many centimeters in 3.7 kilometers?

4. 136 ounces is how many pounds?

   Ⓐ 6.8 pounds
   Ⓑ 8.5 pounds
   Ⓒ 1088 pounds
   Ⓓ 2,176 pounds

5. How many ounces in 5 gallons?

   Ⓐ 128 ounces
   Ⓑ 320 ounces
   Ⓒ 640 ounces
   Ⓓ 1280 ounces

6. Lisa, Susan, and Chris participated in a three-person relay team. Lisa ran 1284 meters, Susan ran 1635 meters and Chris ran 1473 meters. How long was the race in kilometers? Round your answer to the nearest tenth.

   Ⓐ 4.0 km
   Ⓑ 4.4 km
   Ⓒ 43.9 km
   Ⓓ 49.0 km

7. Quita recorded the amount of time it took her to complete her chores each week for a month; 1 hour 3 minutes, 1 hour 18 minutes, 55 minutes, and 68 minutes. How many hours did Quita spend doing chores during the month?

   Ⓐ 3.8 hours
   Ⓑ 4.24 hours
   Ⓒ 4.4 hours
   Ⓓ 5.7 hours

8. Lamar can run 3 miles in 18 minutes. At this rate, how much distance he can run in one hour?

   Ⓐ 0.9 mph
   Ⓑ 1.1 mph
   Ⓒ 10 mph
   Ⓓ 21 mph

9. A rectangular garden has a width of 67 inches and a length of 92 inches. What is the perimeter of the garden in feet?

   Ⓐ 13.25 feet
   Ⓑ 26.5 feet
   Ⓒ 31.8 feet
   Ⓓ 42.8 feet

10. Pat has a pen pal in England. When Pat asked how tall his pen pal was he replied, 1.27 meters. If 1 inch is 2.54 cm, how tall is Pat's pen pal in feet and inches?

   Ⓐ 3 feet 11 inches
   Ⓑ 4 feet 2 inches
   Ⓒ 4 feet 6 inches
   Ⓓ 5 feet exactly

Chapter 3

Lesson 2: Using Properties of Triangles

1. Which of the following lengths cannot be the lengths of the sides of a triangle?

   Ⓐ 4, 6, 9
   Ⓑ 3, 4, 2
   Ⓒ 2, 2, 3
   Ⓓ 1, 1, 2

2. Which of the following set of lengths cannot be the lengths of the sides of a triangle?

   Ⓐ 12.5, 20, 30
   Ⓑ 10, 10, 12
   Ⓒ 4, 8.5, 14
   Ⓓ 3, 3, 3

3. If the measure of two angles in a triangle are 60 and 100 degrees, what is the measure of the third angle?

   Ⓐ 20 degrees
   Ⓑ 50 degrees
   Ⓒ 30 degrees
   Ⓓ 180 degrees

4. Which of the following triangle classifications does not describe the angles in a triangle?

   Ⓐ Right
   Ⓑ Acute
   Ⓒ Equiangular
   Ⓓ Scalene

5. Find x.

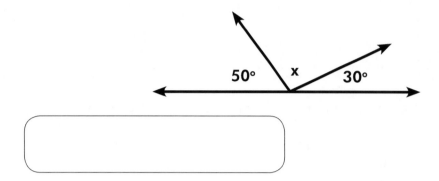

6   Find the measures of the missing angles in the figure below.

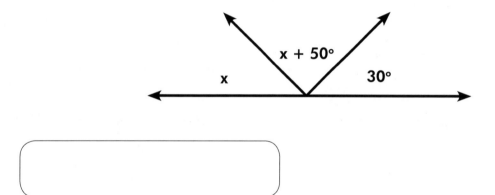

7. The sum of the measures of angles a and b is 155 degrees. What is the measure of angle b?

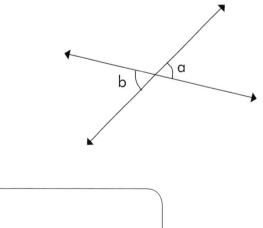

8. **What is true about every pair of vertical angles?**

   Ⓐ They are supplementary.
   Ⓑ They are complementary.
   Ⓒ They are equal in measure.
   Ⓓ They total 360 degrees.

9. **If the sum of the measures of two angles is 180 degrees, they are called ---**

   Ⓐ supplementary angles
   Ⓑ complementary angles
   Ⓒ vertical angles
   Ⓓ equivalent angles

10. **If angle a measures 30 degrees, what is the measure of angle b?**

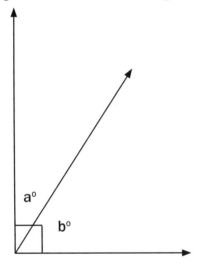

   Ⓐ 60 degrees
   Ⓑ 30 degrees
   Ⓒ 150 degrees
   Ⓓ 20 degrees

Chapter 3

Lesson 3: Area

1. **What is the area of the figure below?**

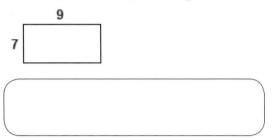

2. **What is the area of the figure below?**

3. **What is the area of the figure below? (Assume that the vertical height of the parallelogram is 3 units.)**

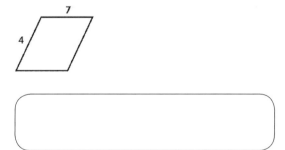

4. The figure shows a small square inside a larger square. What is the area of the shaded portion of the figure below?

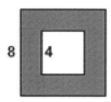

   Ⓐ 64 square units
   Ⓑ 48 square units
   Ⓒ 16 square units
   Ⓓ 80 square units

5. What is the area of the figure below?

   Ⓐ 14 square units
   Ⓑ 28 square units
   Ⓒ 49 square units
   Ⓓ 21 square units

6. What is the area of the figure below? (Assume that the vertical height of the triangle is 2.8 units)

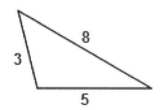

   Ⓐ 15 square units
   Ⓑ 7 square units
   Ⓒ 14 square units
   Ⓓ 40 square units

7. What is the area of the figure below?

5

12

Ⓐ 60 square units
Ⓑ 17 square units
Ⓒ 34 square units
Ⓓ 7 square units

8. What is the area of the figure shown below? The vertical height is 6 units.

19

7

Ⓐ 133 square units
Ⓑ 26 square units
Ⓒ 52 square units
Ⓓ 114 square units

9. What is the area of the gray part of the squares below?.

17   9

Ⓐ 289 square units
Ⓑ 81 square units
Ⓒ 208 square units
Ⓓ 370 square units

10. What is the area of a triangle with a base of 20 feet and a vertical height of 40 feet?

Ⓐ A = 200 square ft.
Ⓑ A = 800 square ft.
Ⓒ A = 400 square ft.
Ⓓ A = 600 square ft.

Chapter 3

Lesson 4: Finding Area, Volume, & Surface Area

1. Find the area of the rectangle shown below.

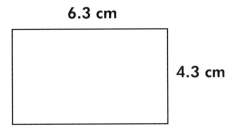

6.3 cm

4.3 cm

   (A) 10.5 square centimeters
   (B) 24 square centimeters
   (C) 27.09 square centimeters
   (D) 21 square centimeters

2. What is the volume of a cube whose sides measure 8 inches?

   (A) 24 in^3
   (B) 64 in^3
   (C) 128 in^3
   (D) 512 in^3

3. Calculate the area of the following polygon.

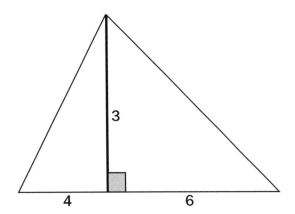

3

4   6

   (A) 15 square units
   (B) 30 square units
   (C) 36 square units
   (D) 18 square units

4. Calculate the area of the following polygon.

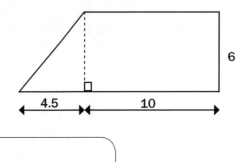

5. What is the volume of the following triangular prism?

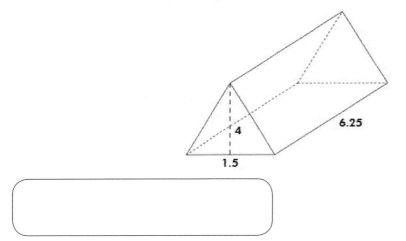

6. What is the volume of a prism with the following base and a height of 2.75?

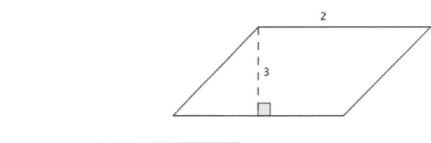

7. **What is the surface area of a cube with sides of length 2?**

   Ⓐ 16 square units
   Ⓑ 8 square units
   Ⓒ 24 square units
   Ⓓ 18 square units

8. **What is the surface area of a rectangular prism with dimensions 2, $\dfrac{1}{2}$, and $\dfrac{1}{4}$?**

   Ⓐ 2

   Ⓑ $\dfrac{13}{4}$

   Ⓒ $\dfrac{9}{4}$

   Ⓓ $\dfrac{3}{2}$

9. **Find the area of the shape below. (Round to the nearest tenth). Use pi = 3.14.**

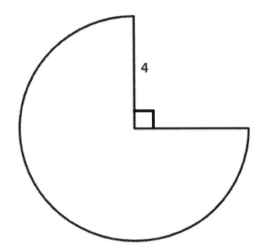

   Ⓐ 37.7 square units
   Ⓑ 50.2 square units
   Ⓒ 18.8 square units
   Ⓓ 35.2 square units

10. John has a container with a volume of 170 cubic feet filled with sand. He wants to transfer his sand into the new container shown below so he can store more sand. After he transfers the sand, how much more sand is remaining in the old container?

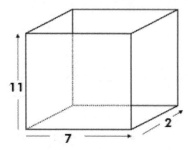

Ⓐ 16 cubic feet of sand
Ⓑ 26 cubic feet of sand
Ⓒ 150 cubic feet of sand
Ⓓ 324 cubic feet of sand

Chapter 3

Lesson 5: Surface Area & Volume

1. **How many rectangular faces would a trapezoidal prism have?**

   Ⓐ two
   Ⓑ four
   Ⓒ six
   Ⓓ zero

2. **Which of the following statements is true of a rhombus?**

   Ⓐ A rhombus is a parallelogram.
   Ⓑ A rhombus is a quadrilateral.
   Ⓒ A rhombus is equilateral.
   Ⓓ All of the above are true.

3. **A cube has a volume of 1,000 cm³. What is its surface area?**

   Ⓐ 100 square cm
   Ⓑ 60 square cm
   Ⓒ 600 square cm
   Ⓓ It cannot be determined.

4. **A solid figure is casting a square shadow. The figure could not be a _____.**

   Ⓐ rectangular prism
   Ⓑ cylinder
   Ⓒ pentagonal pyramid
   Ⓓ hexagonal prism

5. **Which of the following solid figures has the most flat surfaces?**

   Ⓐ a cube
   Ⓑ a triangular prism
   Ⓒ a hexagonal prism
   Ⓓ a pentagonal pyramid

6. **Identify the solid given its net:**

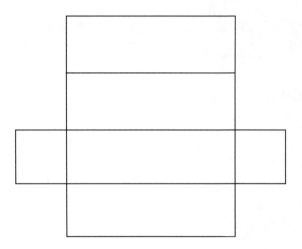

    Ⓐ Rectangular prism
    Ⓑ Cube
    Ⓒ Triangular prism
    Ⓓ Sphere

7. **Identify the solid given its net:**

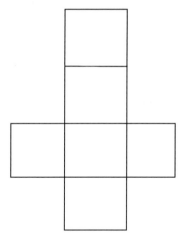

    Ⓐ Cube
    Ⓑ Sphere
    Ⓒ Rectangular prism
    Ⓓ Square pyramid

8. **Identify the solid given its net:**

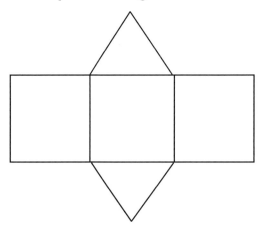

   Ⓐ Rectangular prism
   Ⓑ Cube
   Ⓒ Triangular prism
   Ⓓ Sphere

9. **Identify the solid given its net:**

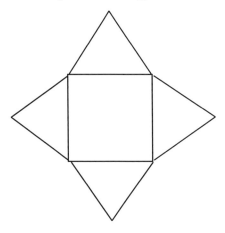

   Ⓐ Cube
   Ⓑ Sphere
   Ⓒ Rectangular prism
   Ⓓ Square pyramid

10. Identify the solid given its net:

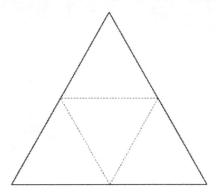

Ⓐ Cube
Ⓑ Sphere
Ⓒ Rectangular prism
Ⓓ Triangular pyramid

End of Geometry and Measurment

Answer Key and Detailed Explanations

Chapter 3: Geometry and Measurement

Lesson 1: Measurement Conversion

Question No.	Answer	Detailed Explanations
1	5.75 feet	There are 12 inches in a foot. 69 inches * $(\frac{1\ foot}{12\ inches})$ = $\frac{69}{12}$ = 5.75 feet
2	31 quarts	There are 4 quarts to a gallon. 7*4 = 28 quarts 28 + 3 = 31 quarts
3	370,000 cm	There are 100 cm in a meter and 1000 meters in a kilometer. 3.7 km * $(\frac{1000\ m}{1\ km})$ * $(\frac{100\ cm}{1\ m})$ = 370,000 cm
4	B	There are 16 ounces per pound. 136 ounces * $(\frac{1\ lb}{16\ oz})$ = 8.5 pounds
5	C	There are 8 ounces per cup, 2 cups per pint, 2 pints per quart and 4 quarts per gallon. 5 gal * $(\frac{4\ qts}{1\ gal})$ * $(\frac{2\ pints}{1\ qt})$ * $(\frac{2\ cups}{1\ pt})$ * $(\frac{8\ oz}{1\ cup})$ = 640 ounces
6	B	Find the total length of the race in meters: 1284 + 1635 + 1473 = 4392 meters There are 1000 meters in 1 kilometer. 4392 m * $(\frac{1\ km}{1000\ m})$ = 4.392 = 4.4 km
7	C	Find the total number of minutes for the month: 1 h 3 m + 1 h 18 m + 55 m + 68 m = 63 m + 78 m + 55 m + 68 m = 264 minutes. There are 60 minutes in 1 hour. 264 min * $(\frac{1\ hr}{60\ min})$ = 4.4 hours
8	C	There are 60 minutes in 1 hour. 3 miles/18 minutes = x miles/60 minutes 3*60 = 18*x 180 = 18x Divide both side by 18 x = 10 miles per hour
9	B	Find the perimeter by adding all four sides of the garden: 67 + 67 + 92 + 92 = 318 in There are 12 inches in a foot. 318 in * $(\frac{1\ foot}{12\ in})$ = 26.5 feet

Question No.	Answer	Detailed Explanations
10	B	There are 100 cm in a meter and 2.54 cm in 1 inch. 1.27 meters * $(\frac{100 \text{ cm}}{1 \text{ m}})$ * $(\frac{1 \text{ in}}{2.54 \text{ cm}})$ = 50 inches 50 in / 12 in = 4.17 feet = 4 feet 2 inches

Lesson 2: Using Properties of Triangles

Question No.	Answer	Detailed Explanation
1	D	The sum of any two sides of a triangle is always greater than the third side. Here, the sum of 1 + 1 = 2. Since the sum of 1 + 1 is not greater than 2, the lengths given cannot be the side lengths of a triangle.
2	C	The sum of any two sides of a triangle is always greater than the third side. Here, the sum of 4 + 8.5 = 12.5. Since the sum of 4 + 8.5 is not greater than 14, the lengths given cannot be the side lengths of a triangle.
3	A	The sum of the measure of angles in a triangle is always 180°. To find a missing angle, add the known angles and subtract the sum from 180°. (1) 100 + 60 = 160 (2) 180 - 160 = 20. Therefore, the measure of the third angle is 20°.
4	D	Triangles classified by angles are acute (all acute angles), obtuse (one obtuse angle), or right (one right angle). Triangles classified by sides are scalene (no equal sides), isosceles (two equal sides) or equilateral (three equal sides).
5	100	The answer is 100°. Reminder: Angles that together form a straight line are called supplementary, meaning they add to 180 degrees. In this case, 50 + x + 30 = 180 requires an x value of 100 degrees.
6	50 degrees	The answer is 50° and 100°. Angles that together form a straight line are supplementary, meaning their measures add to 180 degrees. In this case, x + (x + 50) + 30 = 180 can only be satisfied by an x value of 50, resulting in angles of measure 50 and 100 degrees.
7	77.5 degrees	The answer is 77.5 degrees. When two lines intersect, they form vertical angles, which are equal in measure. Angle a and angle b are vertical angles. To find the value of angle b, divide 155 by 2. The quotient is the value of angle b: 155 ÷ 2 = 77.5 degrees.
8	C	Vertical angles are congruent angles formed by two intersecting lines. The sum of the angles can be less than or greater than 90 degrees and 180 degrees, respectively, so they are not necessarily complementary or supplementary angles. Also, vertical angles do not form a complete circle, so they do not total 360 degrees.

148

LumosLearning.com

Question No.	Answer	Detailed Explanation
9	A	Two angles are supplementary if the sum of their measures is equal to 180°. The sum of the measures of the angles cannot be greater than or less than 180°. It must be exactly 180°.
10	A	The answer is 60°. Angles a and b form a right angle, which measures 90°. This means that angles a and b are complementary. To find the measure of angle b, subtract the measure of angle a from 90: 90 - 30 = 60. Therefore, the measure of angle b is 60°.

Lesson 3: Area

Question No.	Answer	Detailed Explanations
1	63 square units	Area of a rectangle = length x width. A = 9 x 7 A = 63 units²
2	36 square units	Area of a square = (length of side)². A = 6² A = 36 units²
3	21 square units	Area of a parallelogram = base x height. A= 7 x 3 A = 21 units²
4	B	First find the area of the larger square. Then find the area of the smaller square. Use the formula: A = (length of side)² to find the area of both squares. A_{large} = 8 × 8 = 64 A_{small} = 4 × 4 = 16 Subtract the area of the smaller square from the larger square to find the area of the shaded portion (64 − 16 = 48).
5	C	Area of a square A = (length of side)² A= 7 x 7 A= 49 units²
6	B	Area of a triangle = (1/2)bh A= $(\frac{1}{2})$ (5*2.8) A= $(\frac{1}{2})$ (14) A = 7 units²
7	A	A=bh A= 5 x 12 A= 60 units²
8	D	A= bh (where h is the vertical height of the parallelogram) A= 19 x 6 A= 114 units²
9	C	Area of a square = (length of side)² Area of the larger square is 17*17 = 289 units² Area of the smaller square is 9*9 = 81 units² To find the area of the shaded portion, subtract the area of the smaller square from the area of the larger square: 289 − 81 = 208

Question No.	Answer	Detailed Explanations
10	C	The formula for the area of a triangle is: $A = (\frac{1}{2})bh$ $a = (\frac{1}{2})(20)(40)$ $a = (\frac{1}{2})(800)$ $a = 400$ sq. ft.

Lesson 4: Finding Area, Volume, & Surface Area

Question No.	Answer	Detailed Explanations
1	C	The answer is 27.09 square centimeters. To calculate the area of a rectangle, multiply the length and width. Multiplying 6.3 × 4.3 = 27.09 square centimeters.
2	D	The answer is 512 in³. The formula for the volume for a cube is V = s³, where s is the length of one side. Multiplying 8 × 8 × 8 = 512 in³.
3	A	The correct answer is 15 square units. To find the correct answer, apply the formula for the area of a triangle, $A = \frac{1}{2}bh$. First, calculate the base by adding 6 + 4 = 10. Next, multiply the base times the height: 10 × 3 = 30. Then, divide the product by 2: 30 ÷ 2 = 15 square units.
4	73.5 square units	The answer is 73.5 square units. This is a compound figure comprised of a triangle and a rectangle. Identify the length and width of rectangle. Apply the formula for area of a rectangle, A = bh or A = lw, and the formula for the area of a triangle, $A = \frac{1}{2}bh$. Then, add the two products together. The sum is the total area of the figure. (1) area of rectangle: 6 × 10 = 60 square units (2) area of triangle : $(\frac{1}{2})$ x 4.5 x 6 = 13.5 square units (3) 60 + 13.5 = 73.5 square units
5	18.75 cubic units	The answer is 18.75 cubic units. The formula for volume is V = BH, where B = the area of the base, and H = height. Since the base is a triangle, the formula is $V = (\frac{1}{2}bh)(H)$. To solve, plug in the numbers: $V=(\frac{1}{2}bh)(H) =(\frac{1}{2} \times 1.5 \times 4)(6.25) = (3)(6.25) = 18.75$ cubic units.
6	16.5 cubic units.	The answer is 16.5 cubic units. The formula for volume is V = BH, where B = the area of the base, and H = height. Since the base is a parallelogram, the formula is V = (bh)(H). To solve, plug in the numbers: V=(bh)(H)=(2×3)(2.75)=(6)(2.75)=16.5 cubic units.
7	C	A cube has 6 square faces. In this particular cube, each face has an area of 2 x 2 = 4 square units. The overall surface area = 6 x 4 = 24 square units

Question No.	Answer	Detailed Explanations
8	B	This prism is made up of 6 rectangles. Two of them are 2 by 0.5, two of them are 2 by 0.25, and two of them are 0.5 by 0.25 The surface area = 2(2)(0.5) + 2(2)(0.25) + 2(0.5)(0.25) = 3.25 square units, or $\frac{13}{4}$ square units.
9	A	The answer is 37.7 square units. First, find the area of the entire circle by applying the area formula—πr^2. Next, multiply the area by $\frac{3}{4}$ in order to find the area of the shape. (1) πr^2 (2) 3.14 × 4² = (3) 3.14 x 16 = (4) Area = 50.24 cm² (5) 50.24 × $\frac{3}{4}$ = 37.68 = (6) 37.68 = 37.7 cm²
10	A	Volume of the new container = l × w × h = 7 x 2 x 11 = 154 cubic feet. Therefore, after transferring the sand, amount of sand remaining in the old container = 170 - 154 = 16 cubic feet.

Lesson 5: Surface Area & Volume

Question No.	Answer	Detailed Explanations
1	B	A prism has rectangular faces connecting the two bases. A trapezoid has four sides, so four rectangular faces are on a trapezoidal prism.
2	D	A rhombus is a parallelogram that is a quadrilateral and is equilateral.
3	C	Since the volume of a cube is found using the formula: V = (side length)^3, the length of each side of this cube would be 10 [V = (10)(10)(10)]. The surface area of a cube is found by finding the area of one face: A = (side)^2, then multiplying by 6, since there are 6 faces, so 6(side)^2. 6(10)^2 = 6(10)(10) = 6(100) = 600
4	C	A pentagonal prism has 5 sides so it would not cast a square shadow.
5	C	A hexagonal prism would have a total of 8 faces. A cube has 6, a triangular prism has 5, and a pentagonal pyramid has 6.
6	A	When the exposed edges are connected a rectangular prism will be formed.
7	A	When the exposed edges are connected a cube will be formed.
8	C	When the exposed edges are connected a triangular prism will be formed.
9	D	When the exposed edges are connected a square pyramid will be formed.
10	D	When the exposed edges are connected a triangular pyramid will be formed.

Chapter 4:
Data Analysis

Chapter 4

Lesson 1: Graphs and Charts

1. Which of the following graphs best represents the values in this table?

X	Y
1	1
2	3
3	1
4	3

Ⓐ
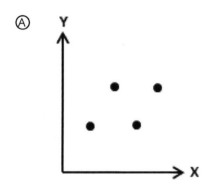

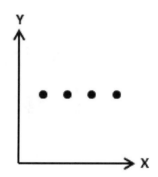

Ⓑ
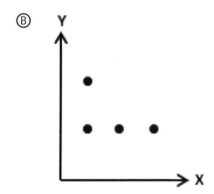

2. The results of the class' most recent science test are displayed in this histogram. Use the results to answer the question. A "passing" score is 61 or higher.

   How many students passed the science test?

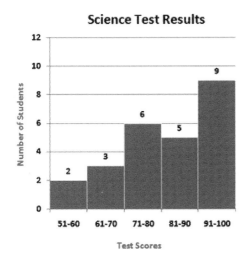

3. The results of the class' most recent science test are displayed in this histogram. Use the results to answer the question. How many students scored a 90 or below?

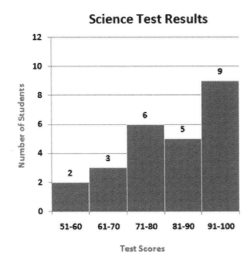

4. As part of their weather unit, the students in Mr. Green's class prepared a line graph showing the high and low temperatures recorded each day during a one-week period. Use the graph to answer the question.

On which day was the greatest range in temperature seen?

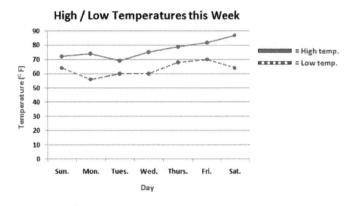

Ⓐ Sunday
Ⓑ Monday
Ⓒ Friday
Ⓓ Saturday

5. The sixth graders at Kilmer Middle School can choose to participate in one of the four music activities offered. The number of students participating in each activity is shown in the bar graph below. Use the information shown to answer the question.

There are 180 sixth graders in the school. About how many do not participate in one of the music activities?

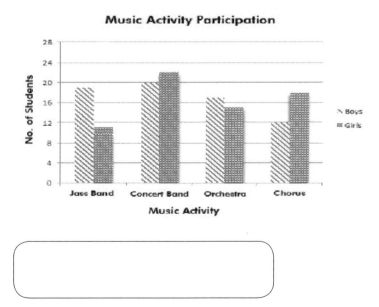

6. A.J. has downloaded 400 songs onto his computer. The songs are from a variety of genres. The circle graph below shows the breakdown of his collection by genre. Use the information shown to answer the question.

Which two genres together make up more than half of A.J.'s collection?

A.J.'s Music Collections

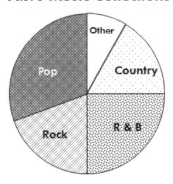

Ⓐ R + B and Country
Ⓑ Country and Rock
Ⓒ Rock and Pop
Ⓓ Pop and R + B

7. The results of the class' most recent science test are displayed in this histogram. Use the results to answer the question.

What percentage of the class scored an 81-90 on the test?

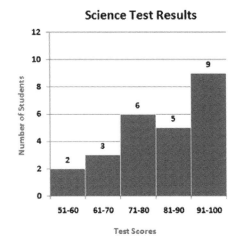

Ⓐ 5%
Ⓑ 20%
Ⓒ 25%
Ⓓ 30%

8. How much of the graph do undergarments and socks make up together?

Clothing Sales Breakdown

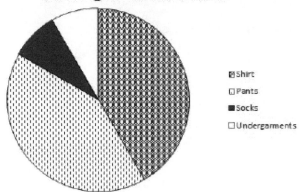

- Shirt
- Pants
- Socks
- Undergarments

Ⓐ less than 5%
Ⓑ between 5% and 10%
Ⓒ between 10% and 25%
Ⓓ more than 25%

9. As part of their weather unit, the students in Mr. Green's class prepared a line graph showing the high and low temperatures recorded each day during a one-week period. Use the graph to answer the question.

What percentage of the days had a temperature of 80 degrees or higher? Round to the nearest tenth.

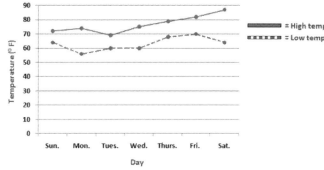

High / Low Temperatures this Week

= High temp.
= Low temp.

Ⓐ 14.3%
Ⓑ 42.9%
Ⓒ 28.6%
Ⓓ None of these

10. The sixth graders at Kilmer Middle School can choose to participate in one of the four music activities offered. The number of students participating in each activity is shown in the bar graph below. Use the information shown to answer the question.

There are 134 students who participate in music activities. What percentage of students who participate in music activities participate in chorus or jass band?

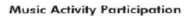

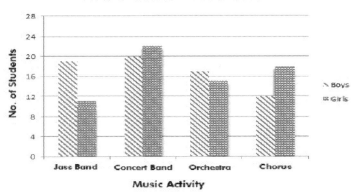

Ⓐ 45%
Ⓑ 38%
Ⓒ 40%
Ⓓ 50%

Chapter 4

Lesson 2: Distribution

1. If the total sales for socks was $60, what is the best estimate for the total sales of pants?

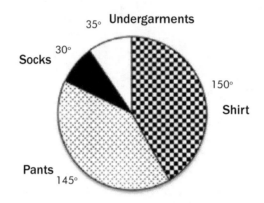

Ⓐ $200
Ⓑ $300
Ⓒ $60
Ⓓ $1,000

Note: Data represent the angles for each category

2. The sixth graders at Kilmer Middle School can choose to participate in one of the four music activities offered. The number of students participating in each activity is shown in the bar graph below. Use the information shown to respond to the following: How many sixth graders are in the Jass Band?

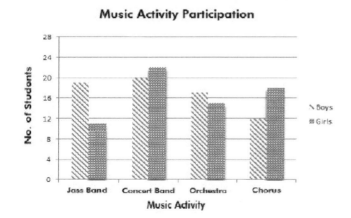

Ⓐ 19 sixth graders
Ⓑ 20 sixth graders
Ⓒ 30 sixth graders
Ⓓ 25 sixth graders

LumosLearning.com

3. A .J. has downloaded 400 songs onto his computer. The songs are from a variety of genres. The circle graph below shows the breakdown (by genre) of his collection. Use the information shown to respond to the following: About how many more R + B songs than rock songs has A.J. downloaded?

A.J.'s Music Collections

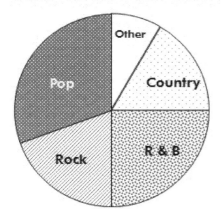

Ⓐ 20 more songs
Ⓑ 30 more songs
Ⓒ 50 more songs
Ⓓ 75 more songs

4. Colleen has to travel for work. In one week, she traveled all five work days. The shortest distance she traveled was 63 miles. The range of miles that she traveled was 98 miles. What is the longest distance that Colleen traveled for work in one week?

Ⓐ 161 miles
Ⓑ 98 miles
Ⓒ 33 miles
Ⓓ It cannot be determined.

5. Bob is a mailman. He delivers a lot of letters every day. His mail bag will only hold so many letters. The most letters that Bob has ever delivered in a day is 8,476. The range of the number of letters that Bob has ever delivered is 6,930. What is the least number of letters that Bob has ever delivered in one day?

Ⓐ 15,406 letters
Ⓑ 1,546 letters
Ⓒ 1,556 letters
Ⓓ It cannot be determined.

6. Fred goes with Katie to the art sale to try to find a gift for his mother. There are 66 pieces of art for sale. The median price is $280. Fred has $280 to spend. What is the minimum number of art pieces Fred can choose from?

[ ]

7. Joann loves to watch the birds outside of her window. There is a robin that comes back every year to build a nest and lay her eggs. Joann keeps track of how many eggs the robin lays. The first year Joann keeps track, the robin lays 9 eggs and that is the least number of eggs she lays. The range of eggs that the robin has laid is one third the number of eggs from the first year. What is the most eggs the robin has ever laid?

Ⓐ 21 eggs
Ⓑ 12 eggs
Ⓒ 14 eggs
Ⓓ 27 eggs

8. Matt loves to watch movies. He has a movie collection that has 285 movies in it. The length of time of all of his movies range from 48 minutes to 3 hours and 26 minutes. What is the range of the length of time of Matt's movies?

Ⓐ 3 hours and 38 minutes
Ⓑ 1 hour and 58 minutes
Ⓒ 2 hours and 58 minutes
Ⓓ 2 hours and 38 minutes

9. Jessica is a photographer. She is putting together photo albums to show off her photographs. The first photo album has 50 pictures in it. The second photo album has 119 pictures in it. The third photo album has 174 pictures in it. The fourth photo album has 72 pictures in it. The fifth photo album has 61 pictures in it. What is the range?

[ ]

10. Sam is a shrimp fisherman. In one month, Sam gets a maximum of 280 pounds of shrimp. The minimum that Sam gets is half of his maximum. What is the range in the pounds of shrimp that Sam gets?

[ ]

Chapter 4

Lesson 3: Summarizing Numerical Data

1. Jason was conducting a scientific experiment using bean plants. He measured the height (in centimeters) of each plant after three weeks. These were his measurements (in cm): 12, 15, 11, 17, 19, 21, 13, 11, 16

   What is the average (mean) height? What is the median height?

   Ⓐ Mean = 15 cm, Median = 19 cm
   Ⓑ Mean = 15 cm, Median = 15 cm
   Ⓒ Mean = 19 cm, Median = 15 cm
   Ⓓ Mean = 15 cm, Median = 13 cm

2. Stacy has 60 pairs of shoes. She has shoes that have a heel height of between 1 inch and 4 inches. Stacy has 20 pairs of shoes that have a 1 inch heel, 15 pairs of shoes that have a 2 inch heel and 20 pairs of shoes that have a 3 inch heel height. Remaining shoes have 4 inch heel height. What is the average heel height of all 60 pairs of Stacy's shoes?

   Ⓐ 1.3 inches
   Ⓑ 1.5 inches
   Ⓒ 2 inches
   Ⓓ 2.2 inches

3. What is the median of the following set of numbers?
   {16, −10, 13, −8, −1, 5, 7, 10}

4. Given the following set of data, is the median or the mode larger?
   {5, −10, 14, 6, 8, −2, 11, 3, 6}

   Ⓐ The mode
   Ⓑ The median
   Ⓒ They are the same
   Ⓓ You cannot figure it out

5. A = { 10, 15, 2, 14, 19, 25, 0 }

Which of the following numbers, if added to Set A, would have the greatest effect on its median?

Ⓐ 14
Ⓑ 50
Ⓒ 5
Ⓓ 15

6. In the last 4 seasons, Luis scored 14, 18, 15, and 25 goals. How many goals does he need to score this year, to end the season with an overall average of 20 goals per season?

7. Stacy has 60 pairs of shoes. She has shoes that have a heel height of between 1 inch and 4 inches. Stacy wants to know which heel height she has the most of. Would she figure out the mode or mean?

Ⓐ Mean
Ⓑ Mode
Ⓒ Both
Ⓓ Neither

8. There are three ice cream stands within 15 miles and they are owned by Mr. Sno.

Ice Cream Stand	Vanilla	Chocolate	Twist
A	15	22	10
B	24	8	14
C	20	16	13

What percentage of the ice cream cones sold by Ice Cream Stand B were vanilla? Round your answer to the nearest whole number.

9. There are three ice cream stands within 15 miles and they are owned by Mr. Sno.

Ice Cream Stand	Vanilla	Chocolate	Twist
A	15	22	10
B	24	8	14
C	20	16	13

What percentage of the ice cream cones sold by Ice Cream Stand C were chocolate? Round your answer to the nearest whole number.

Ⓐ 30%
Ⓑ 32%
Ⓒ 33%
Ⓓ 62%

10. Alexander plays baseball. His batting averages for the games he played this year were recorded. What is the batting average he had the most often?

{.228, .316, .225, .333, .228, .125, .750, .500}

Ⓐ .228
Ⓑ .316
Ⓒ .750
Ⓓ .333

Lesson 4: Data Interpretation

1. How much will the mean increase by when the number 17 is added to the set? Round your numbers to the nearest tenth.

   {5, -10, 14, 6, 8, -2, 11, 3, 6}

2. Andrea plays the violin. She is practicing songs for her concert and she times how long it takes her to play each song. She wants to put the song with the middle number of minutes at the beginning of her concert. How many minutes is the song that she will play first?

   {13, 8, 4, 16, 3, 9, 11}

   Ⓐ 13 minutes
   Ⓑ 11 minutes
   Ⓒ 8 minutes
   Ⓓ 9 minutes

3. There are three ice cream stands within 15 miles and they are owned by Mr. Sno.

Ice Cream Stand	Vanilal	Chocolate	Twist
A	15	22	10
B	20	8	14
C	24	16	13

What percentage of the total ice cream cones sold were twist? Round your answer to the nearest whole number.

   Ⓐ 26%
   Ⓑ 24%
   Ⓒ 62%
   Ⓓ 14%

4. Amy is trying to find out the number of magazines that have a woman on the cover. She goes to the book store and looks at the rack of magazines. There are at least 30 magazines. Amy looks at the covers of 20 magazines. Did Amy get a good sample?

Ⓐ Yes, because she looked at all of the magazines.
Ⓑ Yes, because she got a sample of more than half of the magazines.
Ⓒ No, because she did not looked at all of the covers.
Ⓓ No, because she looked at less than half of the magazines.

5. Travis is putting together outfits for work. He has 4 red shirts, 8 blue shirts and 7 white shirts. He has 6 pairs of khaki pants. What percent of Travis' possible outfits have blue shirts? Round your answer to the nearest whole number.

Ⓐ 8%
Ⓑ 43%
Ⓒ 42%
Ⓓ 48%

6. A new sandwich shop just opened. It is offering a choice of ham sandwiches, chicken sandwiches, or hamburgers as the main course and French fries, potato salad, baked beans or coleslaw to go with them. How many different ways can a customer have a sandwich and one side order?

7. Karen has a set of numbers that she is working with. {6, 14, 28, 44, 2, −6} What will happen to the mean if she adds the number −8 to the set?

Ⓐ The mean will decrease.
Ⓑ The mean will increase.
Ⓒ The mean will stay the same.
Ⓓ It cannot be determined.

8. Susan goes to the store to buy supplies to make a cake. What is the average amount that Susan spent on each of the ingredients she bought?
    {$4.89, $2.13, $1.10, $3.75, $0.98, $2.46}

    Ⓐ $5.22
    Ⓑ $2.55
    Ⓒ $2.25
    Ⓓ $2.50

9. Robert had an average of 87.0 on his nine math tests. His scores on the first eight tests were {92, 96, 83, 81, 94, 78, 93, 70}. What score did Robert receive on his last test?

10. Terry is playing a game with his brother and they played 5 times. The median score that Terry got was 37. The range of Terry's scores was 40. What was the lowest and highest score that Terry got?

    Ⓐ 37 and 77
    Ⓑ 10 and 50
    Ⓒ 17 and 57
    Ⓓ Not enough information is given.

Chapter 4

Lesson 5: Statistical Questions

1. The chart below shows the participation of a sixth grade class in its school's music activities. Each student was allowed to pick one music activity.

    How many boys are in the sixth grade?

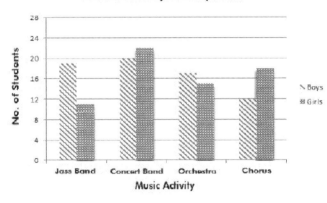

Music Activity Participation

2. **A student wanted to know what the sixth grade girls' favorite song was. What would be the best way to conduct a survey?**

    Ⓐ Do an Internet search of favorite songs of young girls.
    Ⓑ Survey the sixth grade boys.
    Ⓒ Survey the sixth grade girls.
    Ⓓ Conduct a survey at the mall.

3. **Emily wanted to know what the range of daily temperatures this past week was. What would be the best way of conducting her survey?**

    Ⓐ Take the temperature once during the week.
    Ⓑ Take the temperature only in the morning.
    Ⓒ Take the temperature only in the evening.
    Ⓓ Take the temperature two times a day, at the warmest and coolest times of the day.

4. **Goldie wants to find out how many presents children get for their birthdays. She surveys 11 families in the same neighborhood to find out how many presents their children get. Did Goldie get a representative sample?**

Ⓐ No because she did not ask the right questions.
Ⓑ No because she asked families in the same neighborhood who most likely have similar income levels.
Ⓒ Yes because she asked families in the same neighborhood who most likely have similar income levels.
Ⓓ Yes because she asked the right questions.

5. **Roberta is an arborist. She is studying maple trees in a specific area. Roberta wants to show a class the difference in the heights of the trees so that they can compare them. What type of graph would be best for that?**

Ⓐ Line graph
Ⓑ Picture graph
Ⓒ Circle graph
Ⓓ Bar graph

6. **Derek spends an average of 37 minutes a weekday on homework. He wants to know how much time other students in fourth grade spend on homework so he asks only students in his class. Will Derek's survey be biased?**

Ⓐ Yes because he is asking fourth graders.
Ⓑ No because he is asking fourth graders.
Ⓒ Yes because students in his class have the same amount of homework as he does.
Ⓓ No because students in his class have the same amount of homework as he does.

7. **There are five cities in New York State who compete for the title of "The Snowiest City." A survey is done to find the average snowfall. The average snowfall of all 5 cities is 112.6 inches. Cities 1 and 2 both get 116 inches of snow. City 3 gets 110.4 inches of snow. City 4 gets 119.6 inches of snow. City 5 gets 101 inches of snow. Which graph would best represent this information?**

Ⓐ Picture graph
Ⓑ Circle graph
Ⓒ Bar graph
Ⓓ Line graph

8. Brooke is doing a survey to find out what percentage of time families spend together doing activities. She collects all of the data about the time spent together doing those different activities and wants to put it into a graph. Which graph would be best?

    Ⓐ Circle graph
    Ⓑ Picture graph
    Ⓒ Line graph
    Ⓓ Bar graph

9. Peter and Paul are playing cards. They each randomly select 12 cards to start the game. Are the cards that they each selected a biased sample?

    Ⓐ No because they were randomly selected.
    Ⓑ Yes because they were randomly selected.
    Ⓒ Yes because they are not at least 10% of the deck.
    Ⓓ No because they are not at least 10% of the deck.

10. Cara likes to go running. She runs 4 days a week. On Monday, she runs 7 miles. On Wednesday, she runs 3.4 miles. On Friday, she runs 5 miles. On Saturday she runs 7.4 miles. Cara wants to put her data into a graph so that she can visually see the fluctuation in the miles she runs. What graph would be best?

    Ⓐ Circle graph
    Ⓑ Bar graph
    Ⓒ Line graph
    Ⓓ Picture graph

End of Data Analysis

Answer Key and Detailed Explanations

Chapter 4: Data Analysis

Lesson 1: Graphs and Charts

Question No.	Answer	Detailed Explanations
1	A	Using the data to create ordered pairs (x, y), the first choice is the only graph that accurately represents the ordered pairs.
2	23	To find the number of students who passed, add the number of students who scored in the ranges of 61 − 70 (3), 71 − 80 (6), 81−90 (5), and 91 −100 (9). 3 + 6 + 5 + 9 = 23 students
3	16	To find the number of students who scored a 90 or below, add the number of students who scored in the ranges of 51 − 60 (2), 61 − 70 (3), 71 − 80 (6), 81−90 (5). 2 + 3 + 6 + 5 = 16 students
4	D	On Saturday, the greatest range was seen, with a high temperature of 88 and a low temperature of 62, making the range 26 degrees.
5	46	Add together all of the students and then subtract that number from the total number. Jazz: 30 students Concert Band: 42 students Orchestra: 32 students Chorus: 30 students 30 + 42 + 32 + 30 = 134 180 − 134 = 46 students do not participate in any kind of music activity
6	D	Pop and R & B together would make up more than half of the pie chart, or above 50%.
7	B	5 students scored an 81-90 on the test out of 25 students. Convert this fraction into percentage. $\frac{5}{25} \times 100 = 20\%$
8	C	Socks and undergarments together appear to take up more than a tenth, but less than a quarter, of the pie chart. The percentage would be between 10% and 25%.

Question No.	Answer	Detailed Explanations
9	C	Friday and Saturday both had temperatures of 80 degrees or higher. That means that $\frac{2}{7}$ days were 80 degrees or more. Convert $\frac{2}{7}$ into percentage by multiplying $\frac{2}{7}$ with 100. $$\frac{2}{7} \times 100 = 28.57\%$$ Round to the nearest tenth making the percentage 28.6%
10	A	Jazz Band: 19 + 11 = 30 students Chorus: 12 + 18 = 30 students 60 students participate in either jazz band or chorus. To find the percentage, divide 60 by 134. $60 \div 134 \approx 0.45$ To change the decimal to a percent, move the decimal point to the right two places. $0.45 = 45\%$

Lesson 2: Distribution

Question No.	Answer	Detailed Explanations
1	B	The Socks section has a measure of 30 degrees and the Pants section has a measure of 145 degrees. Solve for the total pant sales by setting up a proportion and solving. $$\frac{145}{30} = \frac{x}{\$60}$$ $(145)(\$60) = 30x$ $8700 = 30x$ $290 = x$ Therefore, 300 is the best estimate.
2	C	The graph shows that there are 19 boys and 11 girls participating in the Jazz Band. $19 + 11 = 30$ sixth graders altogether
3	A	Angle corresponding to R + B songs = 90 degrees. The number of R + B songs downloaded is $400 \times (\frac{90}{360}) = 400 \times (\frac{1}{4}) = 100$ songs ($\frac{90}{360} = \frac{1}{4}$ after taking GCF 90 out of both the numerator and denominator) Angle correspoding to rock songs is close to 90 degrees but less than 90 degrees. Let us take it to be 75 degrees (approximately) So, number of rock songs downloaded is $400 \times (\frac{75}{360}) = 400 \times (\frac{5}{24})$ = 83 (approximately) ($\frac{75}{360} = \frac{5}{24}$ after taking GCF 15 out of both the numerator and denominator) Therefore A.J. has downloaded $100 - 83 = 17$ more R + B songs than rock songs. Among the choices given, (A) is the most appropriate choice.
4	A	To find the longest distance Colleen traveled, add the shortest distance to the range. $63 + 98 = 161$
5	B	To find the least number of letters that Bob has ever delivered, subtract the range from the largest number. $8,476 - 6,930 = 1,546$ letters

Question No.	Answer	Detailed Explanations
6	33	The median price is $280 and there are 66 pieces of art for sale. That means that half of the pieces of art have a price of $280 or less. Fred has $280 to spend. That means that he has at least $\frac{1}{2}$ of the pieces of art to choose from. $\frac{66}{2} = 33$ There could be other art pieces priced at $280 above the median so that is why we say "at least".
7	B	To find the most number of eggs laid, add the least number of eggs to the range. The range is $\frac{1}{3}$ of 9 = 3. 9 + 3 = 12 eggs
8	D	The range is the difference between the largest and smallest numbers. To find the range, subtract 48 minutes from 3 hours and 26 minutes. Change 3 hours and 26 minutes to 206 minutes 206 − 48 = 158 minutes Two hours = 120 minutes Subtract 158 − 120 to get 38 minutes remaining That makes 2 hours and 38 minutes
9	124	The range is the difference between the smallest and largest number. The largest number is 174 and the smallest number is 50. Subtract 50 from 174 to find the range. 174 − 50 = 124
10	140	To find the range, subtract the smallest number from the largest number. The largest number is 280. The smallest number is half of 280. $\frac{280}{2} = 140$ 280 − 140 = 140

Lesson 3: Summarizing Numerical Data

Question No.	Answer	Detailed Explanations
1	B	To find the average (mean) height of the plants, the heights would first be totaled. Then the total would be divided by 9 (the number of plants in all). 12 + 15 + 11 + 17 + 19 + 21 + 13 + 11 + 16 = 135. 135 divided by 9 equals 15. The average (mean) height is 15 centimeters. To find the median height, the numbers would be arranged in increasing order. The ordered set becomes: {11, 11, 12, 13, 15, 16, 17, 19, 21} The median is the middle value: 15 centimeters.
2	D	To find the average heel height, first figure out how many of each height Stacy has. Create an equation to figure out the number of 4 inch heels that Stacy has. Add 20 + 15 + 20 + x = 60 55 + x = 60 x = 5 Set up an equation to figure out the mean. You need to multiply the number of shoes and the heel height and then add them together and divide by the number of shoes. $$\frac{1(20) + 2(15) + 3(20) + 4(5)}{60} = x$$ x = 2.2 inches
3	6	To find the median, rearrange the numbers in the data set from lowest to highest. {16, −10, 13, −8, −1, 5, 7, 10} −10, −8, −1, 5, 7, 10, 13, 16 Because this set has an even number of terms, add the two middle numbers together and divide by 2. 5 + 7 = 12 12/2 = 6 6 is the median.
4	C	{5, −10, 14, 6, 8, −2, 11, 3, 6} The mode is 6 because it appears most often. To find the median, list the numbers in order from smallest to largest. −10, −2, 3, 5, 6, 6, 8, 11, 14 The median is 6 because it is in the middle.

Question No.	Answer	Detailed Explanations
5	C	0, 2, 10, 14, 15, 19, 25 Median is 14. (A) If 14 is added to the set, median = 14. So, it does not change. (B) If 50 is added to the set, median = $\frac{14+15}{2}$ = 14.5. So, median increases by 0.5. (C) If 5 is added to the set, median = $\frac{10+14}{2}$ = 12. So, median decreases by 2. (D) If 15 is added to the set, median = $\frac{14+15}{2}$ = 14.5. So, median increases by 0.5. Therefore, median would be affected most by adding the score 5 to the set. Option (C) is the correct answer.
6	28	To determine the number of goals he would need, Luis will need a total of 100 (20 * 5) goals. Set up an equation. Let x represent the goals needed for the 5th season: 14 + 15 + 18 + 25 + x = 100 72 + x = 100 Subtract 72 from both sides. 72 + x - 72 = 100 x = 28
7	B	Stacy would figure out the mode. The mode will tell her which heel height occurs most often when she lists them out.
8	52%	To figure out the percentage, add together all of the ice cream cones sold by stand B. 24 + 8 + 14 = 46 To find the percentage, divide 24 by 46 24/46 = .522 (when rounded to the nearest thousandth) To make the decimal into a percentage, move the decimal point to the right two places and round down. 52%

Question No.	Answer	Detailed Explanations
9	C	To figure out the percentage, add together all of the ice cream cones sold by stand C. 20 + 16 + 13 = 49 To find the percentage, divide 16 by 49 16/49 = .327 (when rounded to the nearest thousandth) To make the decimal into a percentage, move the decimal point to the right two places and round up. 33%
10	A	The number that shows up most often is the mode. .228 is the mode.

Lesson 4: Data Interpretation

Question No.	Answer	Detailed Explanations
1	1.2	To find the mean, add all of the numbers together and divide by 9. 5 + -10 +14 + 6 +8 +-2 +11 + 3 + 6 = 41 41 ÷ 9 ≈ 4.6 (when rounded to the nearest tenth) 5 + -10 +14 + 6 +8 +-2 +11 + 3 + 6 + 17 = 58 58 ÷ 10 = 5.8 When 17 is added, the mean is 5.8 5.8 - 4.6 = 1.2
2	D	Andrea needs to know the median. To find it, list all of the numbers in order from smallest to largest. 3, 4, 8, 9, 11, 13, 16
3	A	To figure out the percentage, add together all of the ice cream cones sold. Stand C: 24+16+13=53 Stand B: 20 + 8 + 14 = 42 Stand A: 15 + 22 + 10 = 47 49 + 47 + 46 = 142 Twist cones: 10 + 14 + 13 = 37 To find the percentage, divide 37 by 142 37/142 = .261 (when rounded to the nearest thousandth) To make the decimal into a percentage, move the decimal point to the right two places and round down. 26%
4	B	In order to get a representative sample, the person who is conducting the survey needs to get a good sample of what they are surveying. Amy looked at 20 magazines, which is more than half (2/3 to be exact)

Question No.	Answer	Detailed Explanations
5	C	Travis has 114 possible outfits. To figure that out you multiply the number of shirts by the number of khaki pants. 19 * 6 = 114 To find the outfits with blue shirts, multiply 8 by 6 to get 48 To find the percentage, divide 48 by 114. 48/114 = 0.421 (when rounded to the nearest thousandth) To make the decimal into a percentage, move the decimal point to the right two places and round down. 42% Alternate Method : Shirts can be chosen in (4 + 8 + 7) = 19 ways. Blue shirt can be chosen in 8 ways. To find the percentage of outfits with blue shirts, divide 8 by 19 8/19 = 0.421 (when rounded to the nearest thousandth) or 42.1% or 42% (when rounded to the nearest whole number)
6	12	Use the counting principle to determine the number of combinations if there are 3 types of sandwiches and 4 types of sides for lunch by: 3 * 4 = 12 There are 12 options.
7	A	{6, 14, 28, 44, 2, −6} the mean is 14.6 {6, 14, 28, 44, 2, −6, −8} the mean is 11.4 The mean will decrease with the addition of the number −8.
8	B	To find the average, add all of the prices together and divide by the number of ingredients, which is 6. $$\frac{\$4.89 + \$2.13 + \$1.10 + \$3.75 + \$0.98 + \$2.46}{6} = \$2.55$$
9	96	To receive an average of 87.0 on the 9 tests, Robert accumulated a total of 783 points. He scored a total of 687 on the first 8 tests. That means his score on the last test was 783 − 687 = 96.
10	D	Just knowing the median and the range is not enough information to figure out the lowest and highest scores.

Lesson 5: Statistical Questions

Question No.	Answer	Detailed Explanations
1	68	Add the number of boys who participated in each activity to find the total number of boys. 19 + 20 + 17 + 12 = 68
2	C	When conducting a survey, it is most accurate to ask the question to the focus group you are trying to reach.
3	D	Taking the temperature consistently at the warmest and coolest time of the day will provide a consistent data sample for Emily's survey.
4	B	A representative sample should be a sample of people who represent the larger population. Surveying all families in one neighborhood would not be representative because people in the same neighborhood most likely have the same income level.
5	D	A bar graph would be best because it shows the data in bars that are then very easy to compare.
6	C	Derek's survey will be biased because the students in his class have the same amount of homework as he does. To get an unbiased sample, he should ask students from all fourth grade classes.
7	C	A bar graph will show the average snowfall of each city in a bar of different colors. Those bars will be very easy to compare and will make it easy to compare the average snowfall.
8	A	A circle graph is the best graph to use when representing percentages. The circle graph would show what percentage of a family's entire day is spent doing each activity.
9	A	The randomly selected cards are not biased. A biased sample is one that contains the same or very similar items. Randomly selected samples are generally not biased.
10	C	A line graph would be best because Cara can plot the miles she runs and connect them with line segments. She will then be able to visually see the fluctuation in the miles (the trend) in the distance she runs.

Questions

Notes

1) **The day before the test,** make sure you get a good night's sleep.

2) **On the day of the test,** be sure to eat a good hearty breakfast! Also, be sure to arrive at school on time.

3) **During the test:**

- **Read every question carefully.**

  - Do not spend too much time on any one question. Work steadily through all questions in the section.
  - Attempt all of the questions even if you are not sure of some answers.
  - If you run into a difficult question, eliminate as many choices as you can and then pick the best one from the remaining choices. Intelligent guessing will help you increase your score.
  - Also, mark the question so that if you have extra time, you can return to it after you reach the end of the section.
  - Some questions may refer to a graph, chart, or other kind of picture. Carefully review the graphic before answering the question.
  - Be sure to include explanations for your written responses and show all work.

- **While Answering Multiple-Choice questions.**

  - Read the question completely.
  - Go through the answer choices.
  - If you are struggling with picking out a correct answer, it is best to eliminate some of the choices. At least try to eliminate two of the choices.
  - Reread the question and find support from the passage to support one of the answers.
  - Recheck the question and your answer.

Note: The Texas STAAR Redesign Math assessments also includes Grid In type questions in the pencil and paper version of the test.

Frequently Asked Questions(FAQs)

For more information on Assessment Year, visit
www.lumoslearning.com/a/staar-faqs
OR Scan the **QR Code**

What if I buy more than one Lumos tedBook?

Step 1 → **Visit the link given below and login to your parent/teacher account**
www.lumoslearning.com

Step 2 → <u>**For Parent**</u>
Click on the horizontal lines (☰) in the top right-hand corner and select **"My tedBooks"**. Place the Book Access Code and submit.

<u>**For Teacher**</u>
Click on "My Subscription" under the "My Account" menu in the left-hand side and select **"My tedBooks"**. Place the Book Access Code and submit.

Note: See the first page for access code.

Step 3 → **Add the new book**
To add the new book for a registered student, choose the '**Student**' button and click on submit.

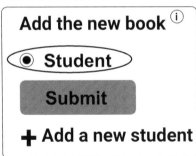

To add the new book for a new student, choose the '**Add New Student**' button and complete the student registration.

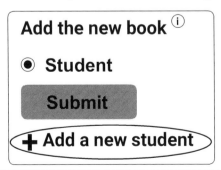

Progress Chart

Standard	Lesson	Score	Date of Completion
TEKS			
6.2 (A)	Classification of Numbers		
6.2 (B)	Opposites & Absolute Values		
6.2 (C)	Using Number Lines		
6.2 (D)	Rational Numbers in Context		
6.2 (E)	Interpreting Fractions		
6.4 (C)	Expressing Ratios		
6.4 (D)	Unit Rates		
6.4 (F)	Represent benchmark fractions and percents		
6.4 (G)	Applying Ratios and Percents		
6.5 (C)	Equivalency		
6.7 (A)	Factors and Multiples		
6.7 (B)	Equations and Expressions		
6.7 (C)	Identifying Equivalent Expressions		
6.7 (D)	Formation of Expressions		
6.3 (A)	Division of Fractions		
6.3 (B)	Numbers multiplied by fractions		
6.3 (C)	Representation of Integers		
6.3 (D)	Division of Whole Numbers		
6.3 (E)	Multiply and divide positive rational numbers		
6.4 (A)	Comparison of Rules		
6.4 (B)	Solve real world problems		
6.5 (A) 6.5 (B)	Solving Real World Ratio Problems		
6.6 (A) 6.6 (B)	Quantitative Relationships		
6.9 (A)	Modeling with Expressions		
6.9 (B)	Representing Inequalities		
6.9 (C)	Formation of Equations		
6.10 (B)	Equations and Inequalities		

LumosLearning.com

Standard	Lesson	Score	Date of Completion
TEKS			
6.4 (H)	Measurement Conversion		
6.8 (A)	Using Properties of Triangles.		
6.8 (B)	Area		
6.8 (C)	Finding Area, Volume, & Surface Area		
6.8 (D)	Surface Area & Volume		
6.12 (A) 6.13 (A)	Graphs and Charts		
6.12 (B)	Distribution		
6.12 (C)	Summarizing Numerical Data		
6.12 (D)	Data Interpretation		
6.13 (B)	Statistical Questions		

Grade **6**

Lumos Learning
Step Up Your Skills

TEXAS
ENGLISH
LANGUAGE ARTS LITERACY
STAAR Practice

Revised Edition

(((tedBook)))
ONLINE

2 Practice Tests
Personalized Study Plan

Available

• At Leading book stores
• Online www.LumosLearning.com

Made in the USA
Coppell, TX
21 May 2024

32649421R00107